FROM A
CAT'S WHISKER BEGI.

The author: Norman C. Cordingly, Wing Commander, OBE,
C.Eng., FIERE, ARPS
Portrait painted by Mollie Cordingly UA in 1946.

FROM A
CAT'S WHISKER BEGINNING . . .

Norman Cordingly, OBE

MERLIN BOOKS LTD.
Braunton   Devon

*This book is dedicated to the
memory of my late wife Mollie
who died on 20th July 1983, in
appreciation of her loving care and
devotion to me during my illness*

*The book is also dedicated
to my two daughters, Juliet and Rosemary*

ISBN 0 86303 431-4
Printed in England by Antony Rowe, Ltd., Chippenham, Wilts.

FOREWORD

by Leonard F. Lamerton Past President of the British Institute of Radiology, formerly Professor of Biophysics Applied to Medicine and Director, Institute of Cancer Research

I have had the good fortune to be associated with Norman Cordingly over a long period — before the war when he was engaged in research and development of medical X-ray equipment, during the war when we both found ourselves members of No. 100 (Bomber Support) Group of the RAF and then again after the war when he was able to return to his consuming interest in radiation and its medical applications.

His memoirs are a fascinating account of some of the great developments over the last 50 years in the applications of science to medicine, and in radar. His own contribution during the war, for which his early training and experience fitted him so peculiarly well, was mainly in the field of airborne radar. Here the combination of his technical skill with a remarkable talent for bridging the divide between scientists, engineers and administrators, on the one hand, and aircrew on the other, enabled him to make an important contribution to the success of operations. But 'Corders' is not only a man of science. He is also an artist who has enjoyed a rich personal life. These memoirs combine the story of technical achievements, descriptions of some of the remarkable — and odd — people he has met, of extraordinary and occasionally hilarious events (the Bostik episode at 100 Group has gone down in history), with a moving account of his personal life.

It is hard nowadays to think of life without radio, television and an all-pervading high technology, but it is salutary to be reminded that not so very long ago life did go on without these things. Norman Cordingly describes those early days and his own first experiments with wireless and later with television, and he remembers the men in his factory working at their treadle lathes wearing bowler hats. He has had a number of 'firsts' to his credit, including the rotating anode X-ray tube, shown at the Science Museum. Throughout his book we see him as someone who is always searching — and sometimes finding. It is a privilege to share with him this account of his life.

Names and ranks in the text are quoted from the author's memory. Ranks are those held at the time described. A fictitious name has been used when the real name is unknown.

CONTENTS

Foreword   5
List of Illustrations   9

1 Happenings during the First World War   11
2 Between the Wars   15
   My Whimshurst machine; Roentgen Society;
   My home-made television; X-ray job at
   Buckingham Palace; X-rays at Royal Academy;
   Restoration of Royal Collection of pictures;
   Deep-therapy X-ray and Diathermy units
   designed; Wedding day
3 Honeymoon as the Storm Gathers   27
   Stay at Ronco; Dance at Bacharach
4 Battling with the Black-out   33
   Westminster Hospital X-ray installation;
   Meeting in the air raid shelter
5 RAF Yatesbury Radio School   38
   Air Ministry Selection Board Interview;
   Radar veil lifted at Yatesbury; Climbing
   the RDF tower in gumboots
6 Life with 604 Night Fighter Squadron Middle Wallop   45
   Night visit to a GCI ground station; Arrival
   of the Magnetron
7 Transfer to 85 Squadron Debden and Hunsdon   52
   New radar homing device — 'Mother'; Havoc
   landing catastrophe; Combat with Junkers 88;
   Corner reflector trials in Dover; Sgt. Jackson
   reported missing; Sherry party at Hunsdon
8 Move to 11 Group — Uxbridge   63
   Theatre outing in black-out; Scharnhorst
   and Gneisenau *incident*
9 I Join the Whitehall Warriors   67
   TRE Research Establishment visits; Submarine
   transport of AI equipment to Malta; Liaison
   with American engineers in connection with
   airborne microwave radar
10 Mysterious Journey   74

11 Mission in the USA   80
    MIT Professor and his tame bear; Visit to
    Naval Air Station, Rhode Island; East Coast
    flight to lecture at Boca Raton
12 Atlantic Flight Homeward   86
    'Sunday Soviet' meetings; Metal foil spoof
    (Window); Flight trials of new SCR 720 AI
    in Mosquito
13 Radio Countermeasures at 100 (Bomber Support) Group   92
    'The Bostik man'; Nuremberg raid — bombers lost
14 The Buzz-bomb Threat and Night Fighters in
        the offensive Role   100
    Flight to Jouvancourt
15 1945: Aftermath Events   109
    Interrogation of Luftflotte-Reich HQ staff
    at Schleswig-Holstein; Visit to radar station
    at Romo; Second visit to Schleswig-Holstein
    and Copenhagen visit; 'Tiger Force' training
16 Posting to HQ Med/ME (Cairo)   123
    Soup surprise at Caserta; Venice and Udine
    visit; Parthenon by moonlight; Christmas in
    Cairo; Holy Land visits
17 Cairo Party Highlights   133
    Farouk the playboy King; The Princess and
    the locust; Pink pied wagtails; The Princess's
    birthday party; Weekend at Faiyum oasis
18 Visit to the Persian Gulf and Luxor   139
19 Back to Civilian Life   141
    Homeward bound on SS Samaria; *Our own home*
    at last; Engineering visit to USA; Rotating
    anode X-ray tube
20 Copenhagen Crisis — and Afterwards   148
    Soft X-ray contact micro-radiographs; New
    post in radiation laboratory — I design
    'clean room'; Retirement

    Nocturn in Retrospect   155
    Epilogue   156
    The passing of Air Vice-Marshal Addison   157

ILLUSTRATIONS

The author	*Frontispiece*
The German bomb that nearly hit author in 1916	12
Family photograph taken at Christmas 1918	14
4-valve wireless built by author in 1924	16
A Whimshurst machine built by author *c.* 1928	19
The author's future wife, Mollie Dale	26
Playing Doppel Kopf by candle-light	28
RAF radar-equipped night fighters in flight —	
Beaufighter, Havoc and Mosquito	44
One of Britain's best kept secrets — the Magnetron	49
John 'Cat's Eyes' Cunningham	51
Wing/Cdr. Peter Townsend and Bill Carnaby	51
The author with his radar mechanics, 85 Squadron	53
Interior of radar operator's rear cockpit in a	
Havoc DB7 night fighter	56
The workshop for servicing airborne radar equipment,	
85 Squadron	60
Flt/Lt. Willis in his radar workshop in Malta	71
Mosquito aircraft showing radome enclosing SCR 720 AI	73
Painting by author depicting interior of a	
Mosquito night fighter cockpit	89
Flying class-room — Wellington aircraft equipped	
to take new AI Mk.X (SCR 720)	91
100 (Bomber Support) Group HQ Signals staff	95
Cartoon by author showing daily inspection by radar	
maintenance mechanics on a Mosquito	105
Cartoon by author showing radio countermeasures	
Flying Fortress	106
Cartoon by author showing Mosquito night fighter	
damaged after shooting down a 'buzz-bomb'	107
Cartoon by author showing radio altimeter being	
calibrated	108
100 Group visit to Luftflotte-Reich HQ at	
Schleswig-Holstein	110
German officer enters Stadt-Hamburg hotel for	
interrogation	111
TRE scientist Dr Cockburn interrogates personnel	
in Luftflotte-Reich HQ	111

German technician with radar equipment   112

Junkers 88 fighter with SN2 radar antennas   112

Junkers 88 with plywood nosepiece to take 9.1 cm
radar scanner   113

Junkers 88 with pointed nose fitted with aerials
for Fuge 218   113

'Tirpitz Tait' and author set off for the Island
of Romo in a German Storch   115

The Mayor of Romo with his wife   115

The Storch's propellor replaced after damage when
landing at Romo   116

A giant German radar ground station (Marmout) seen
at Romo   116

Message and Danish flag left in aircraft by the
islanders of Romo   117

Miss Louisa Dale, aunt of the author's wife, in
the Tivoli tea-shop, Copenhagen   119

Homeward bound on the SS *Samaria* — pen and ink
sketch by the author   142

The author's first prototype rotating anode X-ray
tube, now at Science Museum   147

Micro-radiograph of a dragon-fly's eye taken with
8 kV soft X-rays   151

Painting by author of radiation laboratory showing
neutron generator being lifted out of its
test cell   153

Photograph taken at reunion party — Sam, the author,
Rory and John   156

Note: Photographs and cartoon's illustrated are from the author's own collection. Crown Copyright is acknowledged in certain cases where believed to be applicable.

Chapter 1

HAPPENINGS DURING THE FIRST WORLD WAR

During the First World War when I was a schoolboy not yet in my teens, a fateful incident occurred — I narrowly missed extermination by an enemy bomb launched in a daylight raid by a German aircraft. Fortunately the bomb which had been released failed to explode and I survived to tell the tale.

I was living with my parents at Leigh-on-Sea and one sunny morning I was walking back home along the promenade with my mother, brother and sister. We kept to the seashore side. Everywhere there were signs that we were at war. The railings were festooned with barbed wire entanglement supported by a timber framework. A wounded soldier swathed in bandages and wearing the regulation blue jacket and red tie passed us in his wheelchair, which was being pushed by a uniformed nurse.

The promenade was coming to an end on the Leigh side only a few yards ahead of us when an enemy air raid suddenly took us by surprise. We could see the air battle in progress. Our fighters were in action and there were numerous flak bursts high up in the sky above Southend's long pier. We hurried to get to a concrete shelter which was below a railway bridge. The railway ran parallel with the promenade; the train service using the line started at Fenchurch Street in London and went to Shoeburyness.

As we hurried to the shelter a German aircraft came from the seashore direction, swooping low, and dived towards the bridge. We had just got to the shelter beneath it when a bomb was released. Luckily it did not hit the bridge. We heard the dull thump of the bomb on impact and the sound of enemy aircraft faded into the distance. All was quiet. We waited and wondered what to do next, then eventually decided to go home, which meant crossing the bridge. We did this without mishap and then came to the footpath on the other side. There were obvious signs of disturbance in the soft earth and we saw an evil-looking hole below which the sinister explosive rested.

The next day I saw an Army team busy removing the offending device. Afterwards the bomb, when defused, was displayed in a

*The actual German bomb (supported by a museum official in Sept. 1986)
that nearly hit the author in 1916 during a daylight raid — photographed by
the author seventy years later.
(by courtesy of Southend Central Museum)*

showcase in the Southend Museum. This bomb incident left an indelible impression on me — it was a stroke of luck we were kept safe in the shelter. My lucky escape undoubtedly influenced my actions in the Second World War, as will be seen as my story unfolds.

The Germans made other raids on Southend — some bombs fell on the Victoria Circus Town Centre and caused a considerable destruction of property. Living at Leigh-on-Sea we were always vulnerable to bombing attacks at night by Zeppelins. It so happened that we had a communal air raid shelter at the top of our road in which to seek refuge. The air raid shelter was in an old and disused match factory. The whole building was roofed over by a large water tank. There was space for people to rest with blankets or bedding. We did go to the shelter once when a warning was sounded. However, we and our neighbours soon felt that if any bombs were to be dropped from a Zeppelin it was more likely to be over London. So the shelter became a bit of a white elephant.

On the night of 24th September 1916 a Zeppelin passed over. It was in our vicinity and had crossed the Thames Estuary. It was heading in a westerly direction and we thought the target was likely to be London. The Zeppelin was not yet discernible in the night sky but its three engines could be heard throbbing. We could not sleep as we wondered what was likely to happen. Later my mother called us to come and look out of the bathroom window which faced west. There was a lull for a moment then the night sky suddenly lit up and we saw a great ball of orange flame which lit the surrounding sky with a rosy glow. It was the Zeppelin on fire and we judged it to be not many miles away. We later heard that the Zeppelin had been shot down in flames only five miles away near Billericay, by one of our night fighter aircraft piloted by a Royal Flying Corps Officer. The Zeppelin's crew was killed outright and all the wreckage and debris fell on farmland near by. We thought we were lucky to have escaped a bombing attack ourselves and dreaded the sight of that type of cigar-shaped monster.

When I look back to those grim First World War days I realize I am lucky to be alive to tell the story.

Family photograph, taken at Christmas 1918.
Left: Norman Cordingly, author.
Centre: Eric Cordingly (later became Bishop of Thetford).
Right: Joan Cordingly (later became Matron of Churchill Hospital, Oxford
and then of the Royal United Hospital, Bath).

Chapter 2

BETWEEN THE WARS

The 1914-18 war came to an end and my father, who had been away on war service, came home. I continued my schooling at Westcliff. It was evident that I was bent on a technical career. I always wanted to know what makes a thing tick, and the reasons for results. My thoughts were further influenced by a book given to me one birthday by my godfather Frederick Charles Hart. He was my mother's cousin and was a specialist in optical projection apparatus. The title of the book was *Inquire Within About Everything*. I found it very stimulating. I enjoyed my science lessons at school — we had a charming Senior Science Master wearing a red gown called Dr Peddle. He used to tell us about Marconi and wireless communication. I was very fascinated and was soon spending my pocket-money making crystal sets. I used to wind my own coils. I made condensers and for insulation used toilet paper impregnated with melted candle-wax. I acquired a Hertzite crystal and made a cat's whisker detector. It was a delicate operation to manoeuvre the tip of the cat's whisker over the facets of the crystal in order to pick up various signals, at the same time operating the tuning coils. Imagine the thrill when, as a boy of ten (it was 1920) I received my first 2LO broadcast from London — clearly hearing the voice of Dame Clara Butt singing through my headphones. I was also able to receive broadcasts from Writtle Station at Chelmsford, not far from my home.

Three years later the thermionic valve was available and I constructed a two-valve wireless set. Reception from it was excellent compared with my first crystal set. I became addicted to the wonders of wireless and in 1924 became the proud possessor of a fine four-valve set which I made myself. It was based on a design published by a well-known wireless engineer, Scott-Taggart. I was later to meet him when I was in the RAF Radio School at Yatesbury during the Second World War. I had had the time of my life living during the early realms of wireless. During that period life was exciting; but very soon sadness befell us. My mother, who had been ill for some time, died on the 11th December 1924. Of course, life was no longer the same. I had my future

4-valve wireless, Super Heterodyne ST.100, built by the author in 1924 when he was fourteen years old.

to consider and within the space of three years I was exceedingly lucky to join a scientific instrument makers called Newton and Wright, of Hornsey Road, North London. I continued my technical education and training, taking a General Electrical Engineering Course combined with other Physics subjects at the Northampton Engineering Institute, City of London.

While working in the scientific instrument firm I was to familiarize myself with numerous types of electro-medical equipment in addition to X-ray apparatus, the X-ray tube being the most important item. It required a high voltage to excite it. In addition it had to be made safe by the use of a lead shield to reduce unwanted radiation, which was a distinct health hazard.

Because my mother had died of cancer, I felt that I must do all I could during my life to improve the X-ray equipment usually used for cancer diagnosis, and also for therapy in hospitals fighting this disease. My first job was helping to make the equipment as an apprentice. Later I had a spell in the drawing office of designs, and on planning the lay-out of equipment in hospitals. In those days radiation dangers were not fully understood — many lessons had to be learnt. Safety measures in high voltage were important since the conductors were exposed to both the operators and patients.

Perhaps the most interesting place in the works was the mechanical workshop for making special scientific apparatus. The workshop surely had an old-fashioned air, it really was different from most of the other departments. It was manned by old skilled craftsmen who were often ex 1914-18 war veterans, most of them kept their heads covered by wearing battered old bowlers, green with age. Others wore flat cloth caps. They all had their own lathes which were foot-pedal operated.

An overhead rotating shaft ran the full length of the workshop. It was driven by a flapping length of flat leather belting. Other large machines such as grinders and shapers operated from a belt attachment to the shaft. One noticed that the men were working with brass, either turning on a lathe or shaping by hand with a file. At that time chromium plating was not liked and the men preferred to use a lacquer finish which was applied by camel-hair brush on to the brass that was kept warm with a Bunsen burner. Such instruments as Whimshurst and static machines were fashioned there along with Tesler coils and induction coils, the latter being made in other areas. I was so interested in the Whimshurst machine and was able to learn the know-how so that I could construct one for my own personal use. I lacquered all the parts including the

18

rotating glass plate with metalfoil strips. Both the induction coil and
Whimshurst machine when operated produced a high voltage spark a
few inches in length and when connected to a small evacuated glass
X-ray tube it was possible to produce X-rays for demonstration
purposes. I did my own personal X-ray experiments with my home-
made Whimshurst machine, taking a number of radiographs of birds
and small mammals.

Having enjoyed my work in all departments I was later transferred
to work in the Test Room. This was certainly one step to promotion. I
found the task interesting and it was full of problems demanding time
and effort in general to overcome.

Early in 1928 I was invited to demonstrate a simple X-ray apparatus
at a Boy Scout bazaar held at my home town Church Hall in Westcliff.
The bazaar was to aid the nearby hospital and the local newspaper gave
me plenty of publicity. They took photographs, and under the caption
'X-rays Sixpence a Time' wrote, 'for the modest sum of 6d spectators
could view their bones and at the same time know that they were not
likely to have a leg or arm amputated!'

Working in the firm's department devoted to the testing of
various products designed for new techniques, I was able to keep up
to date. Thus, by moving with the times, I had the opportunity of
visiting many teaching hospitals such as the Middlesex and the
Westminster. I got to know the personnel in charge of the X-ray
department, which included the Radiologist and also the
Radiographers. The latter took the radiographs and had charge of the
photographic dark-room. The Radiologist, of course, was concerned
with the X-ray diagnosis of the patient's ailment and his report was
sent to his medical and surgical colleagues.

The hospital physicist was always an interesting person. His major
task was to ensure that the dose of X-rays applied to a patient
undergoing treatment was in accordance with his measurements and
also to ensure the safety of the patient. It is of interest to note that most
radiological specialists — doctors and engineers and physicists — were
sharing their knowledge and were making outstanding progress in the
X-ray field. In fact it was difficult to keep pace with developments.

At that time there was in being one of England's oldest learned
societies, known as the Roentgen Society. Its headquarters was at 32,
Welbeck Street in London's West End. The society was founded in 1896
following the period when the Dutch-born Scientist Wilhelm Conrad
Roentgen made his great discovery of X-rays at Würzburg University in

A Whimshurst machine built by the author c. *1928 and used with an X-ray tube for his first radiographs.*

November 1895. Practically all our X-ray personnel in the UK were members of this society. (The reader will have concluded that this early history goes back several years before the writer joined the firm to start on his career.)

Attendance at the Institute's meetings was one of the highlights for me. I used to go as a visitor with one of my firm's seniors — Russell Wright (the Managing Director) and sometimes with E.E. Burnside (Director and Engineer). The subjects of the lectures were usually above my head. They mostly concerned X-ray diagnosis in a fairly broad field. Other subjects covered complex aspects of X-ray therapy in general — the fight against cancer was clearly evident. A physicist or a radiotherapist would give a profound evaluation of the work in his particular field. Likewise engineers had an opportunity of reporting on new equipment designed to cope with the latest trends or techniques such as new X-ray tubes and high voltage generators. I should add that one physicist — a radiobiologist — was Dr Leonard Lamerton, whom I often saw at the Institute's meetings — he was to become a good friend in the RAF days during the Second World War.

I was proud to be associated with the X-ray profession from whom I had learned a lot. As engineers we were certainly acknowledged for our expertise and the company, as it continued to thrive, had a great reputation in the British Isles. One day I was summoned to the managing director's office and he told me that I was to be promoted to take charge of the Research and Development department. This was a formidable job and I wondered whether I would be able to cope.

My father and family left Leigh-on-Sea and came to live in North London. They settled in Highgate and I joined them. I certainly had had enough of living in digs! Two years were to pass — I was still having a full and busy time engaged on the supervision of our Research and Development department. Suddenly I had an urge to expand my radio interests. I had been studying the work of John Logie Baird who had demonstrated his mechanically scanned image television in 1926. I went ahead and soon made a circular scanning disc from a flat piece of aluminium sheet. I pierced a number of holes, forming a helix pattern. The disc was mounted on a motor-driven spindle, the end of which had a phonic wheel attached to it. This acted as a synchronizer to help keep the picture steady. The receiver output of my radiogram was just right to energize the neon image tube which one was able to see through a magnifying lens system. When the disc was rotating at the correct speed it made a soft swishing noise which did not upset the sound which issued from the loudspeaker. On Christmas Day that year we all had a hilarious time in the evening watching my home-made machine in action. We were able to discern shapes, the form of which was somewhat blurred and the definition so crude that the thing we saw was anyone's guess! My brother thought the picture was upside down so he stood on a chair and looked through his legs. My sister was behaving like a contortionist and amidst giggles had to give up the guessing game! Our living-room had been turned into a radio laboratory festooned with cables and instruments, nevertheless we all had a happy Christmas, enjoyed our own pantomime, and I had at least been able to produce a moving image!

The Research and Development department was concerned with most problems from high voltage engineering to vacuum tube engineering, including glass manipulation technology. Russell Wright's cousin Tom Wright, himself a mechanical engineer, handled most mechanical designs associated with diagnostic apparatus such as mobile units with special tilting mechanisms. Tom Wright was a delightful character — older than me, he was very tall and had a large moustache which had waxen tips at its ends. Often one started to discuss design problems and invariably finished up by talking about white mice!

Whilst working in my new capacity I am glad to say I had personnel who tackled their tasks admirably. I had several unusual jobs to perform over and above my usual duties — I will endeavour to relate a few of them.

In 1936 King George V, aged 70, was seriously ill with a chest complaint. Whilst remaining at Buckingham Palace he was to have an X-ray which was to be carried out by the Chief Radiologist of the Middlesex Hospital. A portable X-ray unit was used for convenience, to be delivered to the side entrance of the palace in a plain van. This was for security reasons in order to avoid leakage of the King's illness to the press. I was instructed to visit the palace and to meet a palace official to discuss arrangements for the installation of X-ray film viewing equipment. This was to be placed in the Indian Room and was to be used by the radiologist during consultation with Queen Mary. My hurried visit to the palace that particular morning had been marred by an unexpected police speed-trap which I encountered whilst driving in great haste through Regent's Park. At that time the speed limit had recently been reduced to 20 m.p.h., and although I felt I was not guilty because of the urgency of my mission, I was summoned for exceeding this.

When I had completed the arrangements at the palace, I was escorted out of the building by a person whose job, I gathered, was concerned with general maintenance work in the household. We went out via the Ballroom where I was able to see a collection of antiques which had been acquired by Her Majesty the Queen. We also went through the basement. I was interested to hear my escort's story about the palace tap washers — apparently there were enough hand wash-basins and bathrooms to justify one man doing the special job of replacing all leaking washers! That is the story I was told, though no doubt the situation has now been rectified.

There was yet another task in London which demanded my services. This was an occasion when there was an exhibition of Dutch art held at the Royal Academy, Burlington House. Certain art critics and Royal Academicians had decided that a number of exhibits ought to be X-rayed to ascertain whether or not they were forgeries or authentic masterpieces. My firm was enlisted to help and we constructed a tubular steel framework with a travelling gantry allowing an X-ray tube to move horizontally so that its vertical beam of radiation impinged on a painting below in the horizontal plane. We were to work with Mr Kennedy North, well known as an art picture restorer. All the work was done in the lofty vaults below the Academy. We arrived at midnight and worked all through the night, taking a series of X-ray films which covered the painted area on the picture canvas. We returned to the firm's photographic dark-room early in the morning and processed our night's work. It was exciting to see the developed films and to note such features as brush marks of varying clarity depending upon the quality of paints, some of which contained elements which were opaque to the passage of X-radiation. There was a particular painting which was suspect — I cannot remember the artist's name, but it was evident that the X-ray investigation was worth while. I remembered this occasion when, some time in the 1970s, I saw these vaults again. This time I was there as an amateur artist to hand in my paintings for the Summer Exhibition Selection Board.

Our reputation for assistance given to the Royal Academy was to lead to a request for helping Kennedy North again, in 1931, this time in connection with his task of restoring the royal collection of pictures of 'The Triumphs of Caesar' by Mantegna in the Orangery at Hampton Court Palace. It would seem that he had taken upon himself an almost impossible task for the paintwork of most pictures was in a pretty poor state. They had deteriorated because of adverse atmospheric conditions. In some areas the paintwork had blistered and was lifting. The Government Works Engineering Department had erected a large waterproof hut for the whole restoration project. A tubular steel gantry of the type used at the Royal Academy was erected. The X-ray tube could be moved horizontally so that the vertical beam of X-rays covered almost the whole area of the large picture canvas to be examined. A horizontal area of the picture was squared up and a series of X-ray films was taken. These could be placed side by side for reference during the restoration process.

When developed, the X-ray films gave an excellent clue as to brush marks and certain dense areas indicated types and quality of paint. The restorer would wish to know whether the paint contained heavy elements such as lead or zinc. I do not profess to know all about the complex processes which Kennedy North used — all I can say is that a quantity of solvents and new canvas was involved and a huge wooden frame of picture size to take the canvas which had a thick layer of wax adhering to it. The original layer of paint had by some miracle been made to adhere to the surface of a new canvas. When I last saw the paintings installed in a new air-conditioned area they looked in really excellent condition and were a joy to behold. I marvelled at Kennedy North's meticulous work over several years. There can be no doubt that the use of X-rays contributed towards the preservation process, enabling one initially to see modifications made by the artist.

Back in our Research and Development department there were mechanical designs of motor-driven tilting X-ray tables to be used for gastro-intestinal exploratory work and for X-raying most areas of the anatomy. We had perfected new diagnostic X-ray generators using thermionic valve rectifiers. This late equipment superseded the outmoded Snook mechanical rectifiers which had given excellent service but were somewhat noisy.

A 200,000 volt deep therapy unit for cancer treatment was also undergoing a final check. This particular equipment was one of my special designs. It had an oil-immersed high voltage generator and external rectifying valves generating constant voltage supply via flexible cables to the X-ray tube. The first unit was installed at the Marie Curie Hospital in Fitzjohn Avenue, Hampstead. I well remember how pleased the radiologist was to have the equipment. She was a Scottish lady called Dr Riach. After my return from active service I believe I heard that the Marie Curie X-ray therapy department was destroyed by enemy bombing. A number of these 200 KV therapy units, I am pleased to say, were installed for the treatment of cancer in the Middlesex Hospital. I enjoyed handing over the units to Professor Brian Windeyer, the Radio Therapist. Professor J.E. Roberts, Physicist in the Barnato Joel Laboratory, was present at the time. It was always a great treat to join him there for the odd occasional chat.

In addition to these important projects we had a request to design a diathermy unit for bloodless surgery. This was a formidable task, calling for close liaison with surgeons and the study of medical literature. The Americans had a unit using a thermionic valve oscillator. It was deemed to be versatile but was in fact difficult to use since its output was too high powered. We were aware of our problems, a high frequency current had to be generated. The system had to be shock-free and must not have any Faradic characteristics which might cause muscular twitching whilst making an incision. In a few months we perfected a circuit. It was fairly straightforward — my past radio engineering knowledge helped. The apparatus generated a few thousand volts of high frequency from a micro spark-gap oscillator enclosed in a safety shield. Its wavelength was in the radio broadcast region medium waveband. The bloodless cutting controls consisted of a foot switch for the surgeon. Instead of a scalpel the surgeon held a pencil-shaped plastic rod with a flexible cable connected to the end. On the other end of the rod was fixed a chuck which gripped a cutting electrode, usually a tungsten wire or a needle. When this was drawn across the tissue surface it made a clean incision and very little blood flowed. If a capillary was severed it was very quickly sealed with the electrode touching a pair of forceps gripping the vessel. Incisions were practically bloodless due to the sealing action of the electrode in contact with the blood vessels, thus limiting the spread of infection or secondary cancer.

To test the cutting quality of apparatus I used to have in my laboratory a large quantity of rump steak. A piece of steak was placed on an earthed metal plate to simulate operating theatre conditions. While cutting with the electrodes with such an arrangement it was possible to study the degree of coagulation of the severed surfaces, so essential for bloodless surgery depending on the nature of the tissue.

To test for muscular twitching I used to cover my hand with a piece of pliable tin, on top of which I placed a thick steak. The tin would protect my hand should the electrode cut too deeply. Of course, the presence of Faradic sensation could be detected by the use of a cathode ray oscilloscope, whereas the back of the hand gave satisfactory results for test purposes.

Using a loop-shaped electrode attached to a device called a resectoscope it was possible to cut tissue under water. Operating on a prostate gland was successfully carried out by filling the bladder with distilled water which acted as a partial insulator to the high frequency electric current used by the electrode.

The brief encounter I was to have within the realms of surgery certainly made a deep impression on me. My surgical diathermy was made in a portable form and I travelled all round the British Isles meeting eminent surgeons in their operating theatres. We usually had a sample of fresh steak available for them to use while observing the making of incisions with the apparatus. I was to witness many major operations of the brain, lungs and abdomen, and many mastectomies.

After all this travelling my next project at work was the design of shock-proof X-ray tubes. I now wanted time to settle down, and to consider the situation as a whole.

It was my usual habit to have lunch at a 'Joe Lyons' tea-shop in Crouch End — a few minutes' walk from our engineering works in Hornsey Road. I invariably walked up Hornsey Rise and then down Crouch Hill, thereby passing the Hornsey School of Art, whose students used to flock down the hill and almost take over the Lyons tea-shop during the lunch hour. On one occasion I was lunching with an engineering colleague and we beheld two lady art students sitting at a table opposite us. They were engaged in a lively conversation and certainly drew my attention. One of them had lovely eyes. She had a soft voice and exquisite chestnut hair which almost touched her shoulders. I could not resist so rudely staring at her. Our eyes met and I was conscious of a faint smile. I knew we were 'tuned' to the same wavelength!

Some months were to pass, then I had the opportunity to attend a conversazione given by the Art School. It was a great occasion for me as I was formally introduced to the lady, whose name was Mollie Dale. Her father, F.R. Dale, CBE, DSO, MC, was a distinguished classical scholar and Headmaster of the City of London School. Suffice it to say that Mollie and I later became engaged. She was a wonderful artist and was expert in the use of most media.

Later in the 1930s Europe was disturbed because Adolf Hitler was on the rampage. It seemed as if we may be on the brink of another World War. Mollie and I were naturally very concerned about our future wedding plans; we decided to go ahead and fix the date. I had a large programme of work but eventually the long awaited date — 17th September 1938 — arrived and we were married in the lovely Wren Church of St Bride's, Fleet Street. We had a beautiful service with music sung by the Temple Choristers. The reception was held at the

City of London School which stands only a stone's throw from St Bride's. Looking out through the large windows of the Headmaster's study we had a superb view of the Thames, with Blackfriar's Bridge to the left. The reception over, we said goodbye to relatives and friends. They all showed concern for our safety, knowing that we were embarking on a trip through the Continent and that Hitler was still stirring up trouble.

The author's future wife, Mollie Dale, photographed on their engagement.

Chapter 3

HONEYMOON AS THE STORM GATHERS

We travelled in my own motor car, a Riley Nine Monaco saloon. We drove to Dover and crossed at night to Ostend. In the morning our car was hoisted up from the ship's deck and was lowered by ropes with metal shoes gripping the wheels. Unfortunately, during the lowering process the car was almost dropped on to the quayside, it went down with an awful thump. I was naturally concerned, hoping the suspension had not been damaged. It behaved itself whilst we drove along the Belgian cobbled streets so all seemed to be well. We passed through Belgium and were soon in France on a beautiful sunny autumn day. *En route*, between Reims and Châlons-sur-Marne, we stopped to see the 1914-18 battlefields at Fort de la Pompelle. The First World War trenches and tangles of barbed wire were intact whilst the area was overgrown. We stayed the night at Langres and next morning crossed the frontier into Switzerland. We arrived at Corseaux-sur-Vevey and continued on to Zermatt. So far we had been without news of any activity in Germany, simply because in those days we did not have a car radio. We wanted to see the Matterhorn in all its glory and went through Stalden and then Gornergrat. We were able to get a lift up to the Saas Fee glacier where there was a superb view of the Matterhorn, its formidable peak pierced a passing wisp of cloud. We then travelled through the Simplon Pass and crossed the Italian frontier. We stayed in Domodossola — here there were obvious signs of military activity. We heard the local radio and gathered all was not well, and Mussolini was bellowing through loudspeakers in the square. Ironically 'forthcoming events cast their shadows before'. We were anxious to get away from the military atmosphere and to continue our journey onwards to Ronco, a small place reached by climbing a mountain road with serpentine bends. Ronco was a really lovely place to spend a honeymoon — it overlooked Lake Maggiore and we had good accommodation at the Pensione Zurico where we were well looked after by the proprietor, Coniugi Pelucchi. Each evening the local people came in to play the favourite card game called Doppel Kopf. It was a hectic and noisy game. Air raid

Local people of Ronco play Doppel Kopf by candle-light during an Italian practice air raid black-out. The proprietor, Coniugo Pelucchi, smokes a pipe. My wife Mollie painted this quick water-colour sketch meanwhile.

precautions were in force and the main light was turned off while an air raid practice was in progress. The card game had to be played then by candle-light. This jolly scene fascinated my wife — she promptly got out her paint box and proceeded to paint the scene in water colours.

The radio was working and amidst the general clatter we were able to get the gist of news which did not mention anything to frighten us. There was a powerful searchlight beamed across the lake which kept sweeping across the surface. In spite of the worrying situation and the thought of possible hostilities, the place was peaceful so we planned to stay a week or so. The day after our arrival we set out by car to visit the neighbouring lakes of Stresa and Lugano. Half-way down the winding mountain pass we encountered a post coach in a great hurry so as we came to a short bend we had to brake heavily to allow the vehicle to pass because it had the right of way. Our car lurched sideways and there was a horrible mechanical noise coming from the front nearside. We were fairly near the edge of the road and I hopped out to look underneath the car, only to find a steel leaf spring had broken. Steering was now almost impossible and made the drive down very difficult. I decided to go down in stages by kicking the wheel sideways to change direction. This succeeded and I drove the car down safely until we met the main road junction and parked, uttering a sigh of relief.

My wife and I had to decide what to do next. It was obvious that our trip to the other lakes was now off. I wondered how I could even get the car repaired and decided to call at the local bank. Fortunately the man there spoke good English. I explained our trouble and he said he thought the village blacksmith might help. I explained that we could not speak Italian and asked the nice bank assistant to write a note for us to give the blacksmith. This he kindly did and off we went to find the craftsman who understood our plight on reading the note. He assured us he could easily do a repair by making a set of new leaf springs which he thought would take a few days. We felt very relieved and got local transport back to our hotel. It was on our arrival there that it suddenly dawned on me that the rough unloading of my car on the quayside at Ostend must have caused the damage to its springs.

We had a very happy time in Ronco whilst awaiting the car repairs. One day we had an opportunity to do some painting in water-colours when we had a wide view overlooking the Lake Maggiore. Four days later we saw the village blacksmith — he had done a really first-class job and had fitted a new set of hand-made leaf springs. The car's performance on the road felt fine again so we went back to our hotel, packed our luggage and said goodbye to the proprietor. Thus we left on 29th September after spending a blissful time in Ronco.

Our return journey was to take us back via Bellinzona and then through Switzerland via the St Gotthard Pass to Zug, and then to Winterthur where we hoped to contact Ernst Schweitzer, an expert Alpine climber and friend of the family. We hoped to gather some intelligence as to the general situation in Germany before we were to cross the frontier near Schaffhausen. We negotiated all eight hairpin bends of the formidable St Gotthard Pass without mishap — the car performed excellently with its new springs. At Winterthur our friend Ernst came and joined us for dinner at the Hotel Krone. He said it would be unwise for us to enter Germany: the border was surrounded by the German troops and it would be better for us to wait until we had some good news about Chamberlain's visit to Hitler. So the next day we saw Ernst again and he said radio news was encouraging — Chamberlain had returned to the UK with a peace message so he saw no reason why we should not go ahead with our return journey home.

On the 1st October 1938 we left Winterthur and drove to Schloss Laufen where we were able to get a fleeting glimpse of the majestic Rhine Falls, before leaving at precisely 2.10 p.m. We crossed over the border and on our entry into Germany we were confronted by a milling throng of German soldiers and military mobile vehicles. As we passed they must have noticed the GB plates on the car. They laughed and smiled, and called out, "Ah, the children of Chamberlain!" It was a strange feeling — mixing with our would-be enemies who later on, like leopards, changed their spots!

We drove on through the Black Forest and enjoyed the autumn sunshine. We passed through Freiberg and Baden-Baden, then Bergen on the Rhine. Our next stop was to be Bacharach which is a lovely place, affording a superb view across a bend of the river. We stayed at a small hotel with a terrace looking on to the river. Some years beforehand I stayed there with a friend and we got to know the proprietor called Rudi whose father lived in Cologne. We found the hotel looking fine, just as I remembered it. Around us the whole place swarmed with Luftwaffe who were billeted in the area. As we approached the hotel entrance I was appalled to see an offensive notice saying 'Jews Forbidden'. There was also a picture of a jackboot kicking a poor Jew down a flight of stairs. We entered the hotel and there met Rudi. He was pleased to see us but looked a trifle worried. I glanced to the entrance door and he said, "I am sorry; I was forced by the Gestapo to do it — I know my father would be ashamed" — or something to the same effect.

We were given a very comfortable bedroom with a view looking over the wide sweep of the river. After an excellent dinner I decided to walk along the riverside road and to explore. I knew there was a place where we could get a taste of the local wine. The evening was mild and it was good to be walking without the car. We came across the riverside establishment from which we heard sounds of music played by a group of people. We entered and found most of the tables occupied by uniformed Luftwaffe personnel and a few civilians. A waiter found us a table and went off to get us a bottle of wine. News had suddenly spread that this was an English couple who had just arrived. I regretted my decision to enter the place and I am afraid our evening was completely spoiled. Ever since we entered the room my wife Mollie had been the centre of attention. An airman came up to me, clicked his heels and stood to attention and said, "Excuse me, Sir, may I dance with the lady?" I was amazed and looked at Mollie who said "Yes" and let him and other Germans dance with her in the hope that a scene might not develop, especially as the men were drinking a lot of wine. Mollie spent a large part of the evening being whisked around the room with the band doing overtime. I must confess I was scared with the thought that the Luftwaffe were getting their way and that I had acceded to the first chap's request. Unconsciously I had consumed nearly a whole bottle of wine. Eventually a suitable moment arrived and I suggested to my dear wife that we had better get the hell out of the place. She was quite worn out.

We got back to our hotel: I was feeling the effects of the wine and we hurried to bed. Morning came and I had a rotten hangover. Mollie let me sleep and later that morning she arrived with a superb water-colour painting she had just done. It was the scene I had admired, looking towards the river bend.

Later we continued our journey along the picturesque roadway to Cologne and on the evening of 5th October we were in Belgium where we stayed in Tongres. The hotel turned out to be filthy and the sheets in our bedroom were grey in colour. Next morning our minds were full of thoughts that we must return to England; we had a hectic drive through bad weather. It rained all the time and in the late evening we were in Ostend, but not in time to catch the ferry boat. The next day, 6th October, we embarked and left Ostend on the ferry at 10 a.m. — our feelings of concern about the German crisis vanished in the sunshine. With Dover behind us we sped through the English countryside and arrived safely at the home of my wife's parents in Golders Green. The next day we checked that our new home, a maisonette in Stanmore, was ready for our occupation — all was well. We had to move our wedding presents and to buy some furniture but soon we were well and truly settled in.

Chapter 4

BATTLING WITH THE BLACK-OUT

Our new home, at the top of Stanmore Hill, was only a short walk from Bentley Priory the headquarters of the Royal Air Force Fighter Command. We got to know some of the people living in maisonettes similar to ours, and among them were two Squadron Leaders at Fighter Command. One was an Intelligence Officer and the other Deputy Air Provost Marshal. We all had lock-up garages in the vicinity. The fellow occupying the one next to mine happened to be an Air Commodore Aitken who later, at the end of the Second World War, was to become my chief. Our lives soon followed a fairly set routine; I was back working in my Research and Development department. Very soon Christmas 1938 arrived and the sharp frosts of winter made their presence felt. The water tank in the loft of our new flat burst and our carpets were flooded simply because we had not been told where the water stopcock was to be found. The water company came and found it buried under the lawn!

One favourite walk of ours was to skirt the common and go along a footpath close to the Royal National Orthopaedic Hospital. The Radiologist there, Dr Durward, was a friend of mine. I had equipped his X-ray department and some years earlier had travelled on the Continent with him stopping on the return journey at Bacharach (where my wife and I later became involved with the Luftwaffe at the dance session).

Christmas passed and we were soon in 1939. In the office we were perfecting new designs for high voltage shock-proof flexible cable systems to simplify X-ray room lay-out with safety in mind. Later in the year we gained a contract to equip the new Westminster Hospital with some of our latest diagnostic X-ray equipment. We were by now in a new working environment. The old scientific instrument machine shop, the high voltage transformer and generator department and our X-ray tube manufacturing facilities had been transferred to a new factory site in North Finchley. We still retained the old scientific instrument manufacturing expertise and modern production techniques came into being. The old lacquered brass and polished mahogany had gone forever. We now had an up-to-date vacuum technology working area for

33

the production of new X-ray tubes and rectifying valves.

The glass roof of the main assembly shop area had been boarded over as an air raid precaution. Some of our personnel had started our own air raid precautions team of fire fighters and first aid unit.

On 1st September 1939 the Germans attacked Poland and the blitzkrieg began. In a radio broadcast to the nation on the 3rd September Chamberlain officially declared war on Germany. We were all stunned. I was at home with my wife when I heard the announcement: within a few seconds the air raid sirens sounded. We looked out of the door of our maisonette and listened for the sound of enemy aircraft. We also grabbed our civilian gas masks which were packed neatly in cardboard boxes with shoulder strap tapes. My wife reminded me that she had been instructed to report for duty to her nearest first aid station which was at the bottom of Stanmore Hill. On arrival we were surprised to find that most of the women there were wearing their gas masks. We were reprimanded for not wearing ours and amidst the general commotion I said there was no sign of enemy bombers and all was silent. No gas had been released — I thought the sirens had been sounded as a test exercise. We returned to our home.

I went off to my works and on arrival looked up at the newly boarded-over roof. There were a number of barrage balloons aloft. Plans were now afoot to start on the Westminster Hospital X-ray installation. I decided to take with me one of my engineer colleagues who had developed an electronic exposure timer which we hoped to check for accuracy when our new X-ray generator was installed. The electricity company had provided us with a main switch and with this we fixed an electromagnetic overload circuit breaker to be coupled to our new high power generator. Our installation engineers had done a good job since we had arranged to site all high voltage equipment in suitable areas in the basement for general safety. Our preliminary new equipment trials entailed a number of days of fairly hectic work and we had constantly to walk to the basement and then to the X-ray diagnostic department on the ground floor. On one particular day during the new equipment trials I arrived at the hospital in the early afternoon and had parked the car in a side street. The basement atmosphere was a little claustrophobic so we were in need of fresh air at certain stages between our tests. We went outside into the autumn sunshine only to hear the chimes of Big Ben. This caused my thoughts to shift to the Houses of Parliament and the business they had on their agenda. We also wondered what was 'cooking' at No. 10 now that we were on a war footing. Evening came and we decided to snatch a snack. We then returned to start our experiments which were so engrossing that we were not aware of the time passing. When I eventually emerged from the hospital it was quite dark and I stepped out into the street realizing that I had a wife and baby daughter in our new home who would be wondering what had happened to me.

For a moment I stood on the kerb and tried hard to force my eyes to pierce the awful blackness of that October evening; it made no difference whatsoever. Then I looked up the street in the direction where I knew I had earlier parked my car before entering the hospital, the entrance of which was immediately behind me. There were, of course, no street lights for they had been extinguished ever since the ARP regulations were issued at the outbreak of war. Looking down the street in the direction of the Thames Embankment I was conscious of the presence of the slow-moving traffic. One could distinguish the sounds of gear-changing as the London buses approached the roundabout at the junction of the Embankment and Lambeth Bridge, and the well-known 'honk' of the London taxi-cab punctuated the din now and then. Once again I stared hard but I could see nothing for, although the Thames Embankment was barely a hundred yards away, the lights of the vehicles were meagre since by law they had regulation horizontal slit-masks attached to them.

Turning round, I slowly made my way up the street in search of my car. Occasionally it was necessary to shuffle my feet to feel the rough edge of the granite kerbstones, thus enabling me to steer a straight course to my objective. Soon something told me that I must only be a few paces from the car and instinctively I held my hands out in front of me and moved forward a pace. Sure enough my fingers came into contact with the curved after-end of a motor car. It was the sense of feel that very soon enabled me to identify, firstly, the make of the car and, secondly, that it belonged to me. By scratching the metal-plated handle of the offside door with my finger nail I found the little rough patch where the metal plating had peeled off — yes, it was mine all right! I had often found this little scraping trick with a finger nail a very useful one in the black-out — in fact, I frequently used it to identify the smooth edge of a penny sandwiched between some half-crowns when trying to find the correct coin to give a newsvendor in return for the 'Late Extra' paper.

A feeling of comfort came over me when eventually I found myself sitting in the car. The prospect of a twelve mile drive at a snail's pace through London to my home, however, made that feeling of comfort short-lived, for in those days London was so completely blacked out. We had only been at war with Germany a little over a year and, for the last few weeks, London had been visited frequently by the German air force. This was only a foretaste of the enemy's feelings for mankind, but little did one realize the magnitude of things that were to follow. It was strange, I thought, as I started the car, that the air raid sirens had not already wailed their warning of the approach of the death-dealing raiders for I had heard Big Ben chime eight o'clock only a few moments before. On other nights such as this, when the sky was heavily overcast with cloud with no moon, the enemy had usually chosen to raid earlier. In fact, the siren should have gone at least half an hour before. Perhaps the weather was bad on his own airfields, making flying impossible.

There was no difficulty in finding my way up Whitehall. The street was wide and straight but special care had to be exercised when approaching Trafalgar Square, particularly when wending my way through the one-way traffic in order to find the right point at which to turn left to get to Lower Regent Street. Before I reached the top of Lower Regent Street the traffic lights, just twinkling stars, changed to red. Yes, red for danger. At that moment, above the comparative quietness of the procession of vehicles circumnavigating the sandbagged pyramid enclosing Eros, the sirens wailed their warning, only to be followed by the distant boom of guns.

In one way the sounding of the alert and the presence of hostile aircraft was of great assistance to me, as the searchlights fanning the overcast sky lit the streets for miles ahead of me. Thus time passed quickly. I was home in no time. The air raid was still going strong when I alighted from my car and, still with that tense sort of feeling within me, fumbled in my pocket for the keys to open the garage door. Once again I reminded myself of my stupidity. If I had had a torch with me it would have made life so much more pleasant. Fumbling for the right key I again reminded myself that precisely the same procedure would have to be gone through when I eventually reached the front door of my own house. However, things were not so bad. I had found my car by the sense of feel: why not apply the same tactics again? Of course, it would work for, in my mind, I could see the profile of the two keys quite clearly and my sense of feel would connect the two. At that moment a searchlight swept the sky, its beam being cut short by a low-lying cloud above me. Thus all was well. The car was safely locked away and I was in time to enter the house as the beam from the searchlight was doused.

I went upstairs only to find a note saying that my wife and baby daughter Juliet had left for the safety of the air raid shelter. I decided to join them. Our maisonette was in Springfield Close, a small side road just off the top of Stanmore Hill. The actual shelter was the boarded over basement cum wine-cellar of a long building with white-painted timber cladding. It had a clock tower with the usual weather-cock. The owner was a kindly middle-aged gentleman. During air raid alerts he wore the regulation steel helmet and often went on duty as a fire-watcher. In his garden, by the entrance gate to his property, there had been constructed a blastproof sandbagged dug-out. During a raid I often went on duty there with him. We were sometimes joined by RAF officers who were living with their wives in the close. As well as night duties in the shelter I was tempted to join the local defence volunteers, (which later became the Home Guard). A company was formed with the local men: we were issued with khaki denims and .303 rifles. We went to Bisley for rifle practice and underwent a form of combat training. In addition to my usual duties with my own firm's projects I had quite enough on my plate, although the night duty stint during air raids was an essential extra task.

One evening whilst on duty I was joined by a squadron leader whose wife and daughter were in the shelter. We got talking and he showed great interest when I said I was an X-ray engineering specialist. He cross-questioned me and eventually said, "A fellow with your technical knowledge and qualifications ought to be in RAF Fighter Command." That night I gave the matter much thought. I told my wife I thought I ought to do something to help to stop the bombing. It had been in my mind for some time. I also remembered the bomb incident in the First World War. The next day I had a word with Russell Wright, my managing director. He said he did not want to stand in my way and agreed I should do whatever my conscience led me to do.

Chapter 5

RAF YATESBURY RADIO SCHOOL

Soon afterwards I wrote to the Air Ministry and offered my services. I had a quick reply instructing me to attend a selection board interview. When the time came I reported to the Air Ministry, an awe-inspiring array of officials seated on chairs at a long table confronted me when I was ushered into the room where my ordeal was to commence. I walked straight across the carpeted floor towards the man in the centre of the inquisitors, stood to attention, and the Chairman bade me sit on the solitary chair facing them. Simple questions were hurled at me about my schooling, the sort of technical work I was doing, and so on. I handed the Chairman a letter which was written by my managing director which, in effect, said I was doing an important technical job in his company's engineering development department and he did not want to lose me. The Chairman and the rest of the chaps read the letter and without any more ado I was told the letter contained information they were looking for, so I blessed Russell Wright. He had sown the seeds which enabled me to start off in the right direction! I was asked to call at another office where I met a legal type: I guess he was a barrister. He asked a few questions and hinted that the job I was likely to be offered as a commissioned officer was shrouded in secrecy and I would be hearing from the Air Ministry again.

Very soon I received a letter dated 20th November 1940 from the Under Secretary of State saying, 'I am commanded by the Air Council to inform you that they have approved your application for a Commission in the Royal Air Force for Technical Duties', etc. I was appointed with the rank of Pilot Officer, and it would be necessary for me to provide myself with a uniform. I was to report for duty on the 8th December 1940 to the RAF Radio School, Yatesbury.

It was abundantly clear that I would only have a very short time as a civilian before reporting for duty with the Royal Air Force. My first concern was to settle my wife and baby daughter safely. We arranged to move straight away into my father-in-law's house in Golders Green. It had been standing empty since September when he (the Headmaster) had evacuated the staff and boys of the City of London School from London to live with Marlborough College in Wiltshire. We moved from Stanmore to Golders Green and my next job was to get a Morrison shelter installed on the floor of the kitchen, tucked away close to the walls. This was a wise move from the safety aspect as later on, during the enemy bombing of London, the house suffered a near miss when it was ringed by three bombs which fell very close together within a radius of 100 feet and demolished at least three houses. There was also another day when I received a message that the Golders Green house had been damaged by a nearby bomb blast. On inspection I found a number of the windows had been shattered and some tiles on the roof had been lifted. I was able to get hold of my firm's carpenter who came and boarded the windows up and did other essential repairs. Of course the garden was littered with debris scattered from the explosion which had demolished the neighbouring house. I found a large bit of plumbing — a lead pipe and brass coupling bit belonging to a wash-basin — embedded in the brickwork of the garage walls! Such an incident really was diabolical. I was thankful that my wife and the family were away at the time.

We were also concerned about our maisonette and managed to let it to a Fighter Command flight lieutenant and his wife for the duration of the war. We did not like the idea of leaving all our treasured wedding presents which were part of the deal when letting the flat furnished.

I felt I ought to have a break before I embarked on my new mission, so we arranged to travel up to Scotland to stay at the home of my wife's sister Nora who had a beautiful home on the Ochil Hills at Menstrie in Clackmannanshire. Our host and brother-in-law, Alan Porteous, was a very kind and generous person. We spent much of our time walking on the hillside above the house.

My last day as a civilian came all too soon. I then left for London. On 8th December 1940 the new chapter in my life started as I set off by car wearing my new uniform. I had left London in good time and in the evening I arrived at Yatesbury. The Radio School looked imposing with a number of lattice radio masts clustered together pointing skywards. I reported to the guardroom and was soon outside the officers' quarters. I signed on, found my bedroom and then looked for the Officers' Mess. It had a comfortable and businesslike atmosphere. I wandered into the ante-room only to find it was occupied by a mixed bag of chaps, all sporting their new uniforms, the lowest rank being that of Pilot Officer, so I was just one of the 'birds of a feather'! There were about 20 men who had been selected to attend the course. They came from all walks of life, mainly radio engineers from industry, ex-schoolmasters with science degrees, physicists, and a few of varying age groups. We all gathered together and tried to speculate as to just what our tasks would involve. It was dead certain that there was a new weapon of high priority and we would have to wait until the morning when work would start in earnest.

Next day we assembled in the lecture room and were given an outline of the 'set-up' by a F/O Martin. He was to become our guide, philosopher and friend. The school was commanded by a wing commander who was a very helpful and pleasant person. There were facilities for practical work using new equipment. It transpired that we would be working with a new and very secret weapon called RDF (Radio Direction Finding). Its other name, in general terms, was radiolocation. When Churchill conferred with Roosevelt at a later stage of the war the name was officially changed to RADAR by mutual agreement.

The star lecturer at the Radio School was Group Captain Raymond George Hart, of the Air Ministry Directorate of Signals. He was Chief in Charge of RDF and came to lift the veil that shrouded the secret weapon. We were shown a map of the British Isles on which various points on the coast were marked as being CH* and CHL** stations; there must have been about 40 in number. They were part of our early warning system which, through a filter room, passed information of approaching aircraft to HQ Fighter Command at Bentley Priory in Stanmore. The CH station's tall lattice towers had an antenna which radiated high power pulsed radio signals. It had a beam with wide coverage, looking in the direction of the coast occupied by the enemy. Just like the flying behaviour of bats, the transmitted RDF pulsed signals were reflected or bounced off the surface of an object such as an aircraft approaching our shores. Likewise the CHL behaved in the same manner, as part of the early warning system ground stations. Thus all reflected signals picked up by our station's receiver network were passed to HQ Fighter Command via a filter room. The extent of an enemy aircraft raid could be assessed, then Fighter Command would alert its squadrons and trigger off the British air raid warning siren system. The RDF ground stations were controlled by No. 60 Group RAF. It may be of interest to the reader to learn that the CH ground stations with high transmitting towers were the cause of travellers' curiosity. They were sometimes called 'Death Ray Transmitters' and one newspaper published a story which suggested that the huge radar towers around the coast could transmit a strong radio beam

---

* Chain Home   ** Chain Home Link

which was intended to interfere with the ignition of an aircraft's engine and thus upset its flight. There was also a report from a motorist who passed near one of the transmitter towers and his car stopped. He claimed his ignition had been interfered with!

Now to return to the group captain's first lecture to us at Yatesbury. In the second half of this he said that in addition to Britain's RDF ground stations there were a number of RDF devices which worked on the pulsed radio system as employed by the ground station. It was then possible to equip an aircraft with RDF to enable it to detect and intercept any aircraft flying within its minimum range. This equipment was called AI (Airborne Interception). There was another airborne device known as ASV (Air Surface Vessel). Both these devices were compact enough to be fitted in a twin-engined aircraft. The AI equipment had been flight-tested in a Bristol Blenheim and would be operational in the Beaufighter night fighter. This aircraft when fitted with AI was intended to shoot down most of the Luftwaffe bombers. Incidentally ASV was fitted to other twin-engined aircraft for operation out at sea for the detection of surfaced submarines and other enemy ships afloat.

The airborne RDF, such as AI, was a sophisticated new device and had just been issued to HQ Fighter Command twin-engined squadrons. When the group captain had finished his talk, he more or less said, "There you are, gentlemen — take your pick!" Needless to say, I was really fascinated. For a long time I had been concerned about German bombing incidents. There was my lucky escape as a schoolboy during the First World War. Also I had not forgotten the grim sight of devastation caused during the enemy bombing raids in London. All these recollections added up and I informed Group Captain Hart that I wished to take a definite interest in AI. (Later on in my RAF career it was my privilege to serve under the group captain at the Air Ministry, where I was directly responsible for most AI projects in Fighter Command squadrons.)

Most of my brother officers on the course showed an interest in RDF ground stations. My preference was straightforward and I looked forward to working with our own aircrews in the airfield environment. I spent most of my time at Yatesbury studying the 'Black Boxes' containing the secret radio and electronic devices. Sometimes they were called 'Magic Boxes' — a term invented by night fighter air crews, who later had to learn the *modus operandi*.

The airborne RDF, AI, was called Mark IV and operated on a wavelength of 1½ metres. The actual equipment was made in compact and lightweight units. The following is a simple, non-technical description of how it worked. A transmitter aerial shaped like an arrow was attached to the nose of the interceptor night fighter aircraft. It transmitted a high power pulsed radio signal with a wide beam coverage of the sky-zone ahead. It could detect any aircraft flying within the night fighter's AI range. An echo which was reflected backwards was received by two aerials fitted to the ends of the aircraft's wings; one was on the port side and the other on the starboard side. Since the aerials were switched, one could see left or right and detect the echo reflected from an aircraft ahead. The aerial system on the wings could also see up or down, so the received signals were displayed on two cathode-ray tubes, one giving an azimuth indication (right or left) and the other giving elevation display (up or down). The actual received pulsed signals or echoes appeared on the two cathode-ray tubes as a spike on a time base — this spike was generally called a 'blip'. The transmitted pulse bounced off the ground below and was displayed as a large 'blip' at the start of the time base. This was called the ground return. The cathode-ray tubes indicator could be seen through a soft rubber visor which fitted snugly on the operator's face and was light-tight. The AI device had sophisticated and somewhat elaborate electronic circuits and would require good maintenance, demanding the right know-how from the technical back-up.

All of us were able to spend quite a time really getting to know all the complex RDF systems. Of course, the equipment for the CH type ground system was heavy, and one component I have in mind was the MB2. It was British made and was under the control of No. 60 Group personnel.

Initially weather during the course was cold and frosty. We were busy getting to understand the ground station operation and its transmitting aerial array and we had a go at matching the aerial systems. Our task was to climb the moderately high lattice tower. No one fancied doing such a job because of the cold weather. I said I was willing to have a go, not knowing what was in store for me. I was instructed to climb up with a light rope attached to the test gadget on the ground. I was wearing gumboots with thick moulded rubber ribs on the soles. They were ideal, I thought, and would give a good grip on the lattice crossbars. I got to the top and started to swing over to the other side of the tower so that I could reach the aerial feeder wires. I hauled up the test gadget and found I had got my rubber soled boot jammed in a V-shaped gap where the crossbar was fitted to the main upright. There was no time to panic. I was really scared stiff but eventually dislodged my boot. Of course, the chaps at the foot of the tower had a good laugh, although I was not amused. However, by hook or by crook we managed to do the measurements. I contented myself with the thought that I had chosen to work with aircraft and not to act as a permanent steeplejack!

Christmas Day arrived while we were on the course. We all had an excellent time in the Mess; there was one snag, I missed being with my wife and baby daughter. However I did manage to visit my wife's parents not far away in Marlborough afterwards, to glean some family news.

On one occasion during our course we met John Scott-Taggart, a well-known radio engineer and RAF lecturer. A wonderful feeling of nostalgia came over me because some 17 years had elapsed since I first made my four-valve wireless set which was based on a Scott-Taggart circuit design, then known as the ST 100. I began to think we were really improving our technical knowledge listening to Scott-Taggart and all our new weapon circuits were just part of the evolution of new projects to help us to win the war against the Luftwaffe's threat.

It soon transpired that most of the officers on the RDF course were to fit into a rather complex jigsaw pattern. We were all working for the same cause and the aim was certain with mutual understanding, either with ground station activity or on the airfields of Fighter Command.

ROYAL AIR FORCE RADAR-EQUIPPED NIGHT FIGHTERS IN FLIGHT

(a) Beaufighter — 604 Squadron.

(b) Havoc DB7 — 85 Squadron.

(c) Mosquito — 100 Group.

Chapter 6

LIFE WITH 604 NIGHT FIGHTER SQUADRON MIDDLE WALLOP

There came a time when my work on the course was nearing its end: indeed, I was eager to put into practice all I had learnt. My wishes were soon granted when I received instructions from HQ Fighter Command; I had been posted to RAF Station Middle Wallop where I would be attached to 604 Auxiliary Squadron equipped with Beaufighters. I heard they were to be equipped with AI Mk.IV. Well, this was the answer to my prayers! It was mid-January 1941 and I made preparations for my move. I bade my colleagues farewell and after lunch drove my car in a south-easterly direction. During my stay at Yatesbury I had enjoyed the countryside of Wiltshire with its places of historic interest. I was soon in Andover and then right in the direction of Middle Wallop. I had lost a bit of time and arrived later than I had hoped. The Officers' Mess was an imposing brick building. I parked my car and was soon in comfortable surroundings. I had missed dinner and wandered into the dining-room to be confronted by a mountainous cold buffet, all the goodies artistically arranged on a pure white linen table-cloth. I had an excellent solitary meal, and although a little apprehensive I looked forward to sampling life on a fully operational fighter station, which was soon to make history from the night fighter aspect.

I was able later to find F/O Gilfillan, a radio officer with whom I was to work. We agreed to meet again at breakfast next day, and then I went off to bed. Through the silent night I could hear the intermittent sound of aircraft engines from a distant part of the airfield. It gave me a peculiar feeling as I realized that those engines meant business — the battle against the enemy bombers. I found it hard to believe that from now on I was on active service!

Amidst the clatter of china and cutlery I heard the sounds of lively conversation as I entered the dining-room for breakfast. It was fairly well occupied by aircrew, pilots and observers, and a sprinkling of officers of varied seniority. Gilfillan joined me; it was good to meet a chap who was sympathetic to the fact that I was newly fledged and who understood my wish to 'get down to brass tacks'. He was a little older

45

than me and had been with this squadron for a short time. He had a good team of radio mechanics and some of them would now need to be trained, as they were to look after servicing and general maintenance of our special RDF equipment in Black Boxes!

After breakfast I reported to the Squadron Adjutant and then met the Station Commander. We met the Squadron Commander, Sqn/Ldr Mike Anderson too. I was soon able to see a gaggle of Beaufighters parked in the dispersal area. They were all fitted with AI Mk.IV and were painted matt black. The Beaufighter was a formidable looking aircraft. Its nose was blunt and was adorned with the arrow-shaped transmitter aerial. The receiving aerials (dipole) were on the leading edges of the wings. Sqn/Ldr Mike Anderson came up to check the state of the aircraft. Our sergeant in charge of radar mechanics was able to give the 'gen' to the CO when the daily routine inspection on RDF boxes was completed. We inspected a Beaufighter cockpit with its AI indicator unit, complete with visor, which was mounted to the right of the aircraft instrument panel. The radio observer would sit behind the pilot and give instructions to him over the intercom. His assessment, to enable the pilot to engage an enemy, was based on the position of blips seen on azimuth and elevation cathode-ray tubes. Another 'Black Box' was also installed in the aircraft; it was called IFF (Identification Friend or Foe). It was an ideal safeguard to prevent us shooting down one of our own aeroplanes. The IFF, when interrogated by an AI pulsed signal, transmitted a pulsed reply in Morse code. This IFF system was also installed in our own bomber aircraft.

I was next to meet the squadron's night fighter Flight Lieutenant John Cunningham, known as 'Cat's Eyes' Cunningham. He had his radio observer, Pilot Officer Rawnsley, with him. Gilfillan and I completed our tour of inspection. Later in the afternoon the aircrew, whose aircraft had been serviced, would fly their Beaufighters and do a night flying test. They would in all probability carry out an interception, using one of the squadron's own aircraft as a target when airborne. Their means of communication was VHF radio. They were able to receive instructions from 'OPs' controller either from the sector or from a GCI* station near the coast.

The servicing of the AI was time-consuming and Gilfillan and I had a good liaison together. We designed and equipped a special motor vehicle to help to speed up general servicing of our AI. We

---

* Ground Controlled Interception.

carried a petrol-driven electric generator set and a switch panel was constructed from components I had managed to scrounge from my old firm's test department.

One day, before long, I had an opportunity of accompanying F/O 'Rory' Chisholm on a pukka night flying test and was able to experience the sensation of a flight in daylight using our own aircraft as the target. Notes I made at the time in my flying log-book read 'Date 26.2.1941. Pilot: F/O Chisholm. Time 14.20. Beaufighter. Training of operator. Altitude 17,000 ft. Target: Beaufighter. Flying time 2 hr. 30 mins.' During the flight I was positioned behind the pilot and operator and was able to listen to conversations on the intercom. When the operator had well and truly got the hang of the AI we made a gentle landing. I was interested to compare instructions passed on the intercom to the pilot with the position of the target after contact was established. The two cathode-ray tubes had performed well. One had only to imagine how conditions would differ at night with a hostile aircraft as a target! After the war our pilot, Roderick 'Rory' Chisholm published a book called *Under Cover of Darkness*, describing the life at Middle Wallop and the outstanding work of AI-equipped night fighters. It is not my intention to reiterate the incidents which are described in this nocturnal narrative — all I wish to mention are happenings which had a profound effect on me particularly. One should realize that Middle Wallop was my one and only taste of Britain's all-out struggle to beat the night bomber, and enemy casualties were on the increase thanks to our AI interceptor equipment and the skill of its operators. Later in my RAF career I was to find myself attached to a new group headquarters and Roderick Chisholm was its Senior Air Staff Officer (SASO).

On the 13th March 1941 I was able to arrange a visit to our GCI station which invariably controlled the squadron's aircraft when alerted for night flying operations. I met the controller and the staff on duty in the darkened 'OPS' room. There was very little space, for most of the area was occupied by a large circular cathode-ray tube, almost the same size as the conventional TV screen today. This was called a PPI (Plan Position Indicator). The GCI ground station had a rotating aerial which had a fairly narrow beam of pulsed radiation covering a radius of approximately 50 miles. Echoes reflected from all aircraft flying within its range were displayed as small blips on the sweeping time-base. The image had the familiar greenish-yellow fluorescent light which had an after-glow. Thus the position of an aircraft found by a blip could be marked and its movement plotted. Our night fighters could then be given the right course to fly and to intercept the enemy and the positions of bombers and fighters could be assessed.

I was glad I had chosen that evening to visit our GCI station as it turned out to be a Gala night. There was a certain amount of enemy activity and our squadron was airborne. The night sky was clear, with just a little moonlight. A blip was identified as one of our own squadron's night fighters and another aircraft, this time hostile, then appeared. The blips converged as a combat ensued. The controller soon heard from 'OPS' that the pilot, F/O Chisholm, had engaged and shot down an enemy bomber crossing the coast near Bournemouth. Chisholm then returned to base to refuel and rearm. I stayed on to watch the general activity in the coastal area displayed on the PPI. Later that night two blips were again plainly visible over the coast, one identified as hostile and the other as friendly. An interception took place (the blips converged) and 'OPS' confirmed by telephone that Chisholm had 'done it again' and had destroyed another bomber the same night! Everybody in the room cheered with excitement. My memory of the events that occurred the night that Rory scored a hat-trick is a little confused. Apparently the two enemy bombers which he destroyed were Heinkels returning to base, having already dropped their load. In the Mess at lunch-time we congratulated Rory wholeheartedly over the proverbial gin. Inwardly I felt happy and satisfied that the Black Boxes, while in the capable hands of Sergeant Riply (Rory's AI Operator), had done the squadron proud. I forget the squadron's total of enemy destroyed but it was certainly considerable.

I was anxious to have further experience of night flying with AI and its associated demands on the operator. I arranged to fly one night with John Cunningham and his operator F/O Rawnsley; and so on the 10th March 1941 we were airborne in his Beaufighter, Letter R. We flew at 20,000 feet, our task to calibrate the cathode-ray tube time bases. I had an interesting flight and all went well.

During that period of my stay at Middle Wallop we had news of a really outstanding scientific discovery — the Magnetron. This was a super and very special valve oscillator which operated in the centimetre wave band. The Magnetron was the product of research by Oliphant, Randall and Boot in Birmingham. This exciting development put a new complexion on radar and its associated application. Use of the centimetre waveband meant we would have highly accurate detection equipment with very narrow beams. A new AI equipment was under way towards the end of the month and I was soon able to behold AI

One of Britain's best kept secrets — the Magnetron. This picture shows one of the few which were made. The Magnetron here is slightly damaged, having been removed from a crashed aircraft. It is shown approx. double size.

Mark VIII — similar developments using the Magnetron were already on the Ministry of Aircraft Production's plate. A new ASV and another device called H2S had been perfected for installation in our own bombers to aid navigation by locating built-up areas. The AI Mark VIII operated on a wavelength of 10 cms. (S. Band), an ultra-short wave compared with our existing AI Mark IV wavelength of 1½ metres. The new radar was not introduced immediately for obvious reasons. It had to undergo flight trials. It is interesting to note that the major development of radar equipment, both ground and airborne types, started at Worth Matravers near Christchurch. It had been the home of boffins who worked night and day to produce the RDF devices for the Royal Air Force. The writer remembers one occasion when he met Dr Bowen who did considerable development work and perfected AI Mark IV whilst based at Christchurch. Amidst all the excitement of new technical advances and the feeling of not knowing what was to happen next I became a fully fledged flying officer. I was informed by Fighter Command that my services would soon be required by another night fighter squadron in No. 11 Group. A few days before the end of March I heard I was to be posted to No. 85 Squadron, RAF Station Debden. The adjutant of 604 Squadron wished I could stay on a little longer with them. I said I had fresh fields to conquer and felt I had done my share there. I had had an excellent liaison with Gilfillan who was soon to move to a new post.

Left:
604 Squadron
John 'Cat's Eyes' Cunningham (then a
Flt/Lt.) Later, in 1943, he commanded
85 Squadron.

Below:
85 Squadron
Wing/Cdr. Peter Townsend
(centre) and Bill Carnaby
(supporting propeller)
with whom the author flew
during the last raid over London.

Chapter 7

TRANSFER TO 85 SQUADRON — DEBDEN AND HUNSDON

I was due to join my new squadron by the end of April 1941 and had planned a few days' leave. I joined my wife and daughter who had been living in my father-in-law's house in Golders Green. Leave was precious in those days. It was a great thrill to be home in spite of living in a wartime atmosphere full of petty restrictions and ration books. I marvelled at the way my dear wife had coped. All was well with the household and what a contrast it was when compared with squadron life. My short leave vanished all too quickly. I was soon on the road again; my destination was Fighter Command in Stanmore. Previously I had planned this visit to meet Wing Commander George Adams who was in charge of Radio Officer personnel. I drove up Stanmore Hill and at the top stopped and walked into the little side road where our first home stood in Springfield Close. It was in September 1938 when we first moved in there to start our married life. It all seemed strange to me. The maisonette had been let to an officer in Fighter Command and here I was on the very spot where I first made my decision to offer my services to the RAF. I had a good look at the flat, it appeared well cared for; and so I went back to the car and drove to Bentley Priory. I was in time to meet George Adams, a jovial chap. He seemed pleased to have a talk about my activities whilst at Middle Wallop. In civilian life George was a radio engineer who was a 'Big Shot' in the film industry. After a pleasant meeting I set out *en route* for Debden in the county of Cambridgeshire. On arrival at the Officers' Mess I was greeted by my new Squadron Commander Wing/Cdr. Peter Townsend. He was very friendly and courteous. While we were in conversation a number of 85 Squadron aircrew chaps came up and I was introduced as the long awaited man with the Magic Boxes! They were all eager to know all about the operation of the new AI devices which were to be fitted to their aircraft. Most of the aircrew, including the squadron commander, were ex-Battle of Britain pilots who had been flying single-engined Spitfires and Hurricanes. They had had a conversion course to twin-engined aircraft and were then getting to know the characteristics of

The author with his radar mechanics, 85 Squadron. Sgt. Jackson is on author's left.

their new night fighter aeroplanes which were called DB7s. These were Bostons built in America; in the RAF they were called Havocs and, like the Beau night fighters, they were painted matt black. The aircraft had a tricycle undercarriage which gave a smooth landing. There was very little vibration, which sometimes is the cause of damage to intricate electronics apparatus such as the electrodes of cathode-ray tubes.

I met my new Sergeant, Jackson, who was in charge of radio mechanics. He was a very pleasant character with a soft speaking voice. I was very pleased to find we had a full quota of mechanics, mostly leading aircraftmen. They were keen men and first-rate on maintenance jobs. Just as with 604 Squadron, my experience told me we ought to get hold of a mobile vehicle to speed up servicing. I was soon lucky and got a Ford V8 shooting brake. Of course, this pleased Sergeant Jackson.

Most of the Havocs had been fitted with the AI Mark IV. I would now have a fairly busy time flying by day and also have the opportunity to operate at night-time depending on the enemy activity, to train the operators. There had been a lull so all effort was concentrated during the day. Peter was 'cracking the whip' so we did see an intensification of our training programme. Peter liked to get off early in the morning before breakfast. I joined him one day as an observer — we flew with his AI Operator.

Life was enhanced by frequently meeting the numerous flying personnel in the Mess, in particular pilots. I found I had learnt a lot about life in general, and the many facets which stimulate its pattern. I found I was now living in an entirely different environment. Only three years before I had just started married life. I also had a young daughter and certainly missed sharing her early years. However, I was now finding something which enriched my life and I was indeed eager to do all I could by giving my support to the aircrew whenever they asked for assistance.

Various squadron pilots had exceptional qualities; I am glad I had the opportunity to fly with them on special occasions. There was one, James Wheeler, a man with slightly grey hair. He had been a civil airline pilot and was one of the flight commanders. He had a dry humour and his personal operator was an air gunner, F/O Charles Maton. James and Charles were a well matched pair and I flew with them often. Flt/Lt 'Nig' Marshall and Flt/Lt Paddy Hemmingway were keen night fighters. I was privileged to help out on night flying tests and occasionally I flew a night 'op' with them.

We had a new radar device which was called 'Mother'. This was a homing beacon which transmitted a coded pulsed signal when interrogated by the Havoc's AI Mk IV transmission. 'Mother' was ideal: it was essential equipment for any aircraft returning to base, particularly in bad weather, ground mist and the like, and more than once it got us home after special missions. The homing beacon had an operational range of approximately 50 miles radius. My radar mechanics kept it in good order and it was installed on the airfield near our maintenance section.

At this stage of our work on the airfield we tried to assess performance of 'Mother' AI. All was well after a few teething problems had been corrected by Sergeant Jackson. By the way, the operator in the Havoc sat in the rear cockpit using an adjustable stool and was able to look down on to the indicator cathode-ray tubes. Sometimes we had two seats to enable two persons to fly side by side to learn the technique. Entrance to the rear cockpit was through a hatch at the rear with access by a small ladder. Communication between operator and pilot was via an intercom system. I did not like this because it meant isolation from any view the pilot was able to get prior to his carrying out a pukka interception. On the other hand the operator seated in the rear cockpit did have a jolly good view skywards looking upwards through his perspex canopy.

At the end of April the squadron moved to its new airfield at Hunsdon, which had two runways. On the east side of the perimeter track we had a fine, newly built workshop which was the delight of Sgt. Jackson. At the end of the workshops a set of masts was fixed to take the AI transmitter aerial and the elevation antenna. There was enough space for test equipment and stowage of apparatus. I had a full complement of eighteen radio mechanics, and with the assistance of a newly acquired mobile vehicle — a Ford V8 shooting brake — we had all that was desirable to keep the squadron's secret weapon in 'good nick'! I had my private office with other buildings on the west side of the perimeter. The Officers' Mess was a few miles away from the airfield, on a really beautiful countryside site. Our Mess was a mellow brick Georgian style mansion, with ample accommodation for all personnel. We lived comfortably and we fed well. Access to the Mess was via a track bordering a well-stocked lake bounded with lovely trees. Of course, there was some good fishing in the lake and one evening I was clever enough to land a large pike weighing a little less than 18 lb. There was also plenty of wild birdlife and altogether one felt relaxed in that lovely country atmosphere, quite away from the madding crowd. With our airfield adjacent we did, of course, get the full benefit of aircraft engine noise. The flight path was just clear of us.

Interior of radar operator's rear cockpit in a Havoc DB7 night fighter, showing the AI Mk. IV cathode-ray tube indicator unit. The operator's bucket seat is on the left.

One morning in June F/O Evans invited me to join him and carry out the night flying test on Havoc Letter C. On our return flight to the airfield he made a conventional three-point landing but as the aircraft continued along the runway the front wheel support snapped. The propellers made a grinding noise on the concrete surface of the runway, and the aircraft came to a halt. When the nose of the Havoc tipped forward the tail turned upwards; as it did so I was thrown off my seat and shot backwards until my bottom was wedged in the rear of the tail section. All was quiet. I could not talk to my pilot because the intercom was out of reach. I had visions of leaking petrol and the likelihood of fire. After what seemed an age I managed to get myself free, stood up and looked through the rear cockpit perspex canopy. There was still no sight of F/O Evans. However, all was well — the station crash-tender arrived followed by the Station Doctor. He helped to heave me out and I went off to the Medical Room where he checked me over and said that the slight knock on one of my knees was not serious. Fortunately F/O Evans was unhurt. The damaged wheel leg-casting was examined by the Engineer Officer who said there was evidence of a fatigue fracture in the alloy.

Bill Carnaby was the squadron's tallest pilot: he was dark and handsome and keen on his job. On the 11th May 1941 Bill contacted me, I think he said his operator was off sick and he wondered whether I could arrange to fly with him on operations that coming night. I thought it over and was glad to have the opportunity of putting into practice all I had said about our AI. Indeed I wanted a change from the ordinary routine work on the station. So that particular night I was sitting in the crew room with the chaps already dressed in flying kit. We had already tested our AI that afternoon and were all ready for action. As the hours passed aircrew were returning from 'OPS' and they gave us a lively report of enemy activity outside the London area and said that the enemy's main target tonight seemed to be London. Just after midnight we were ordered to be airborne. There was a little moonlight and the weather was warm and fine. 'OPS' controller ordered Bill to fly southwards to skirt the North London area. There was a dazzling array of searchlights sweeping the sky and the balloon barrage was up. We would have to keep well above them and avoid the flak. We approached the North-East part of London and looking downwards through my rear cockpit perspex canopy I beheld an awful scene of devastation below. There were many fires casting an orange glow on a few wisps of passing cloud. Every now and again there were bright flashes from exploding bombs and there must have been large quantities of incendiary bombs being scattered far and wide. A great pall of smoke occasionally obliterated our view. London was certainly burning and I felt grieved that this was the real thing and that all living people and creatures below would be helpless. I thought of my sister Joan, a nursing sister at the London Hospital in the East End. She was certainly in the thick of it and had to cope with a number of casualties, she later told me. I saw a group of bright twinkling lights, obviously incendiary bombs that had fallen on the roof top of a city building. I thought of St Paul's Cathedral and prayed it would not be damaged. I looked into my AI indicator and saw a blip. Obviously the echo from an enemy aircraft. I gave Bill directions. He followed the contact, we were still on the outskirts of NE London. Then it was 'bandit ahead' and we started to close on the aircraft. It was flying fast and had therefore in all probability already dropped its load of bombs. It was weaving a little; I gave Bill left and right directions to correct flight and we straightened out and kept on its tail. As we began closing we were approaching the East Coast and at this point we were in contact with our GCI Controller. He gave Bill a vector and we continued our chase, coming very close now to the maximum range of the AI. We soon got the blip and as we were flying fast I told Bill we should look out. Suddenly he said, "I can see it!" He throttled back and said, "I think it's a Junkers 88." I gave him elevation and azimuth corrections, he put his nose down and increased speed and we started to dive and then climb. He said, "I'm going to fire."

I tried to see ahead through my rear cockpit canopy but could not make out the silhouette of the bomber. Then the whole aircraft vibrated as our 20 mm cannon fired and the cockpit filled with the smell of cordite fumes. Bill shouted, "I think we hit it!" and the bomber disappeared from his view. It was in a dive and flying out to the sea. We wondered whether it would finish up in a watery grave. Our GCI piped up to say, "Good show!" and told us to return to base. Our position was over Orford Ness. I managed to get 'Mother' on the indicator so we were able to home to base. There was a certain quiet as we flew back: I was filled with wonderment. Looking south, the distant glow told us London was still burning. We wished the horrors of war would all come to an end.

We made a good landing and we walked into the crew room and settled down for a night-flying supper. Oh boy! Bacon and eggs and coffee! We were certainly hungry after our tense combat with the enemy.

Vera Lynn, the Forces' Sweetheart, came one evening to sing to us at Hunsdon. Afterwards we entertained her in the Mess. The staircase in that lovely old house was crowded with a group of us who sat near her whilst drinking the odd glass of booze. This was a lovely party for it was good to hear someone who was able to give good cheer to all and sundry. I must admit I too found a space on the stairs to listen to the conversation that ensued. I think I can still hear in my mind the one song among others she sang which was specially appreciated by the ex-Battle of Britain pilots ' . . . . Blue Birds over the White Cliffs of Dover.' By sheer coincidence I had occasion to go to Dover at the request of Fighter Command who wanted me to demonstrate a special swivelling corner reflector which Sgt. Jackson had constructed. The Air-Sea Rescue organization, using high speed launches, was controlled by VHF radio and was plotted by the CHL station at Dover. They wanted to get a good signal to enable them to get a fix on the movement of the Air-Sea Rescue launch sent to pick up aircrew in trouble. We fixed our swivelling corner reflector to the yard-arm of the launch. The mounting of the reflector on the launch ensured a good return echo. The intention was to carry out an exercise to vector the launch in the English Channel well out of range of the enemy warning system.

In the CHL 'OPS' room we watched the 'blip', an excellent signal on the cathode-ray tube. There was no VHF reply and amidst the confusion we wondered what had happened to the launch. The Navy at Dover telephoned, saying they had heard that an enemy aircraft flying low had shot up a launch. It appeared that our corner reflector was good for the goose and also for the gander. The enemy radar had presumably seen the launch on their screen. It was a sad day and we returned to our base. I well remember another sad day when I lost Sgt. Jackson, who died whilst carrying out checks on AI equipment during a daytime night flying test in conjunction with a squadron aircraft acting as a target. I was in the radar workshops when I had a report that the aircraft had not returned to base and that there had been accidents to two aircraft. This was indeed a sad moment for us all and I must place on record the fact that Sgt. Jackson served the squadron well. His quiet way of tackling problems I shall not forget. He was the salt of the earth. Needless to say the radar servicing section had done well and I was quickly able to find a capable mechanic as a replacement.

Early in June 1941 on a glorious sunny evening we had a sherry party at the Officers' Mess in Hunsdon. Quite a number of the local county folk were invited, including the vicar and a number of retired persons who lived near by. They were very pleasant and I imagine it was a good way of indirectly offering apologies for the noise which was present on

The workshop for servicing airborne radar equipment — 85 Squadron.   (Crown copyright photograph)

the airfield, so active when night flying was essential. Of course, a lot depended on whether or not their houses were close to the fighter aircraft path.

Our party included representatives from HQ No. 11 Group and men who were well known at Fighter Command. The squadron mascot 'Kim', a fine Alsatian dog, was much in evidence. He was usually to be found close to Peter Townsend. I remember walking along the lakeside path, the birds were still singing their spring melodies. Across the lake the familiar call of the moorhen could be heard, and as I disturbed a squirrel in the grass it shot up the tree above me.

There was a lady guest at the party. I must confess I do not remember her name. She invited me to come and play tennis at her home, and so another day after duty I went over to play tennis and after a good game we had tea. My hostess came up to me and asked whether I had a relation who was a prisoner of war in Japan. She then said her son was a prisoner there and in his letters he said he had been helped by a very kind army chaplain called Eric Cordingly. Well, what a coincidence! I was able to confirm I was Eric's brother. I explained he was in the Dunkirk disaster and had had a pretty rough time on the beaches during the evacuation. After convalescence he joined his regiment and finished up with his chaps working on the Burma railroad. Needless to say when he did return to the UK he did a mammoth job communicating with the next of kin of the many chaps who suffered and died in that awful hell. I am proud to say he was a great fellow and he later finished up as Bishop of Thetford.

The months were flying by. We had had a beautiful spring and now we were in high summer. The squadron had been on the go almost non-stop. Everything on the airborne radar side seemed to be reasonably free from trouble. Fortunately I had an Assistant Radar Officer, Herbert Howard, attached to me since March. He was an ex-science master and was a keen radio man. We got on well together.

One morning I was greeted by the Squadron Adjutant, Tim Maloney. He had a likeable smiling face. He said he knew one of the county gentlefolk, a lady whose Christian name was Phillida. She had very kindly offered to have an officer and his wife to stay at her home and would I be interested? Of course, I jumped at the idea and went to her house to talk to her. My wife was also thrilled at the idea and without more ado she came to spend a week with me there. Our hostess was a charming person and the house we went to stay in was called Noah's Ark. It was well furnished and we were given a most comfortable bedroom. I was able to have breakfast in the morning and usually I came back from the airfield for dinner so we were in clover. In the evening we were able to relax and sit back to enjoy Phillida's library of Beethoven records. I remember listening to the Pastoral Symphony in that pleasant country setting. The drive to the house was bordered with flower beds which were filled with giant sunflowers. Our young daughter Juliet laughed with happiness and amazement when she saw these huge, tall flowers. All too soon this blissful week in the country had to come to an end and I was back in the Officers' Mess.

It was with considerable sadness that we heard news that Peter Townsend was soon to leave us, as he had been posted for more exacting duties with the Royal Household. Before long our new Squadron Commander, Wing/Cdr. Saunders, arrived to take up his duties. He had a fantastic reputation as an expert in the navigation field. He was also well known for his superb handlebar moustache — it really was the 'Cat's Whiskers'! On the 1st July, I noted in my log-book, I flew on night operations with him. We used the AI Mk.IV but there was no enemy activity to speak of.

Chapter 8

MOVE TO 11 GROUP — UXBRIDGE

On the 7th October 1941 I was to say goodbye to the squadron with whom I had had a happy and indeed exciting time. I had been promoted to the rank of Flight Lieutenant and had been posted for higher duties to HQ No. 11 Group in Uxbridge. I was to have twelve squadron radar officers under my wing to keep them informed of technical changes and also to ensure that the night fighter squadron had the right AI interception device. I was indirectly in communication with Fighter Command staff who were always anxious to hear news of equipment behaviour and the success achieved by its use against the enemy bomber.

It was fortunate that Uxbridge was a reasonable distance from our temporary home at Golders Green. I was able to enjoy family life and to commute to headquarters. Fighter Command HQ in Stanmore was also within easy reach and since my duties would take me to both headquarters it worked out very well. I had a farewell party with all those wonderful fellows in the squadron and then pressed on for home to be with my own family. The next day I reported for duty at Uxbridge. Here I was met by the Chief Signals Officer, Wing/Cdr. Porter, to whom I was to be responsible. I was now a staff officer and had responsibility for administering all group radar officers. My AOC (Air Officer Commanding) was Lee Mallory. He had a distinctive air about him, a well-trimmed moustache, and he wore CB and DSO ribbons.

Enemy air activity was somewhat sporadic. All our night fighters kept up their work and the equipment was undergoing a change because of the introduction of the Magnetron and the era of the centimetre waveband was soon to come. The 10 cm waveband, known as S. Band, was still a top secret, and new and sophisticated airborne radar was under way. H2S, a special 'Black Box', was being installed in bombers and the AI Mk. VIII was on trial in aircraft allocated for centimetric airborne equipment. Rory Chisholm, with whom I had worked at Middle Wallop, was now in charge of Fighter Interception Unit RAF Station Ford. Most of the Government boffins from the Telecommunications Research Establishment (TRE) who worked on our devices at Worth Matravers had moved to a new site, Malvern College, under the direction of a Mr Rowe. A special airfield had been allocated for airborne radar at Defford.

New aircraft would soon be available for the night fighter role. The wooden Mosquito aircraft made by the De Havilland company was already out on trials. An experimental installation had been completed with 10 cm S. Band AI. This state of affairs foreshadowed things to come and squadrons with centimetre AI and radar operators properly trained to cope certainly were good news and heartening. Within a short period the Mosquito was to make its debut. This revolutionary change was to me the most exciting period of my RAF career, which had started with small beginnings. Fighter Interception Unit (FIU) had been formed at RAF Station Ford, not far from Tangmere. The Commanding Officer of the FIU was Wing/Cdr. Rory Chisholm. He had the fascinating job of flight testing aircraft and equipment for Fighter Command. In my new job at 11 Group I often had the opportunity of visiting FIU and of flying with new prototypes. I also made occasional visits to the Telecommunications Research Establishment at its new Malvern College home. Most prototypes of experimental airborne radar aircraft were kept for flight trial at Defford airfield and there was also liaison with the FIU at Ford.

Since my arrival at No. 11 Group I had a very busy time. We had the occasional group meeting which was attended by the majority of our squadron radar officers. So time passed quickly and there were always a few problems warranting attention. However, life did have some moments to let off steam. My wife and I went to a Fighter Command party given by the C-in-C, Sir Sholto Douglas, at Bentley Priory. We were privileged to meet famous men of the RAF, Battle of Britain pilots and other medalled men also, who had distinguished themselves in one form or another. I felt proud to be associated with these chaps from all walks of life, whose main aim was to rid this country from the threat of the Nazi scourge.

Life at that time always seemed a little hectic and we cherished those parts of life which were tranquil. My wife and I were looking forward to an addition before long to our family and one evening we went to the theatre. London had not changed very much, there was the usual black-out which presented some problems when walking on foot. Whilst watching the performance on the stage, believe it or not, the wretched air raid sirens sounded and the distant crack of the ack-ack almost drowned the dialogue. We all stayed put and tried to forget the external uproar. When the show was over I still felt that old feeling and wondered when it was going to end. Walking towards the Piccadilly Underground Station in the black-out, my wife stumbled on the kerb while we were crossing the road. We felt a bit concerned and hoped all would be well.

Travelling on London's Underground in those days I felt appalled at the conditions which the inhabitants had to endure. Certainly the stations made safe shelters but the people had to lie side by side like sardines deep below the ground's surface. It was a really grim picture to see young and old people lying flat and tucked up with blankets on the platform, all trying to get some sleep amidst crying babies and the constant rush of tube trains and hurrying passengers.

1941 was flashing by. It was four months since I first went to No. 11 Group. I had been on a number of official visits to other Command stations which included trials at Wick in Scotland where I flew in Coastal Command Hudsons. New Year arrived with some unexpected news. I found that in King George VI's New Year's Honours List I had been awarded the MBE!

On 12th February 1942 a huge 'flap' started which kept Fighter Command and 11 Group active like an upset beehive. It all happened, I was later told, because of a telephone call made by Group Captain Victor Beamish to our own AOC, Air Vice-Marshal Leigh Mallory. It transpired that Victor, of Sector Station Biggin Hill, was known to go off on his own unofficial dawn patrol in his Spitfire. I believe that on the morning in question he was flying over the English Channel in the vicinity of the Dover Straits. He noticed a considerable amount of shipping activity off the French coast and when he got within visual range he observed some German battleships speeding up the coast. He suddenly realized that this was the long expected attempt by the German Navy to get their battle cruisers, which had been tucked away camouflaged in a dock area, clear of Brest. Victor returned to base on full throttle and on landing rushed to the telephone to break the news to the AOC. Telephones were in action all day. We had a call from one squadron reporting that its AI night fighter radar had been jammed, making interception of their target difficult because of radio interference which apparantly originated from the direction of the French coastal area. So night flying tests had to be abandoned pending further notice. We also heard that our ground-based stations on the coast looking seawards were really in trouble and were almost inactive. This catastrophe caused us a big blow! The RAF was active all day and the Royal Navy ordered its torpedo-carrying Swordfish aircraft to attack whilst the battle cruisers *Scharnhorst* and *Gneisenau* and the *Prinz*

Eugen were belting at high speed up the French Coast. The German radio interference could not be stopped immediately by us. It is interesting to note Winston Churchill's remarks in his memoirs — *2nd World War, IV, 'Hinge of Fate'* p.105: 'By February 12th, however, the jamming had grown so strong that our sea-watching radar was in fact useless.' There was one thing which was obvious to most of us — our night fighter radar would have to operate on a frequency which was unlikely to be jammed; so all the top secret 'S' band microwave radar work in the pipeline was now the answer worthy of consideration. The need for counter-measures was outstanding in our minds. Would such be forthcoming in time?

My future work caused me some worry. Anyway most decisions in a wartime atmosphere had to come from above and via our distinguished boffins. We were exceptionally happy to learn that the research and development progress at TRE Malvern really was proceeding apace. Furthermore, the Ministry of Aircraft Production too was almost 'flat out' in an endeavour to get new microwave radar equipment available for airborne work, in addition to ground station detection. Of course, the new Magnetron, operating in the ultra high frequency band was the heart of S band equipment operating at 3,300 MHz and was already part and parcel of AI Mk. VIII fitted in Beaufighters, in conjunction with a parabolic reflector with a common transmitter/receiver antenna.

A further important development was that of the new Mosquito aircraft. There were many reasons for introducing it for night fighting, apart from its other uses in Bomber and Coastal Commands. All this evolutionary technology caused great excitement and enthusiasm.

Early in 1942 I was promoted to the rank of Squadron Leader and was posted to the Air Ministry, where I was thrilled to find I would be working indirectly for Group Captain Hart, Radar Chief on the staff of the Director General of Signals whose head was Air Vice-Marshal Sir Victor Tait. I was thankful that I would be able to live at home with my family and drive to Whitehall to my challenging new job. I felt I now had an all round experience of life on an operational night flying station and I had good technical contacts at FIU Ford and at the Telecommunications Research Establishment which would be useful.

Chapter 9

It was early spring as I went to get my car out on the day I was to join the 'Whitehall Warriors'. The rear of the brick-built garage backed on to the garden and access to it was through a side door fitted with a mortice lock, and overlooking a rosebed and sizeable lawn. I tried to insert the key and found the keyhole was filled with some substance which offered considerable resistance and I just could not use the key. My next move was to unscrew the cover plate; I found much to my surprise that the keyhole and its mechanism was stuffed solid with daisy heads! Fortunately I always carry a penknife with me so I was able quickly to extricate the offending floral obstruction. At that time my language was not that of a gentleman! I guessed that the cause of the trouble was my two-year-old daughter Juliet. She admitted she had posted the daisy heads 'in the letterbox'! I had to laugh and was thankful that I had such a clever young child.

My route to Whitehall was straightforward, and my Hillman Minx was pretty nippy in the West End traffic. On entering Trafalgar Square I turned off into Whitehall. The distant view of Big Ben cheered me. Passing the Cenotaph I had to turn right to enter King Charles Street where I found a suitable place to park my car. The guard on duty challenged me and I explained I had not yet been issued with the official pass. In the Directorate of Signals I was ushered into my new office which was very well furnished with the usual filing cabinets, not forgetting the umbrella stand with bracket for hats and coats. The waste-paper bin was also sitting proudly in the corner. My next objective was to meet again Group Captain Raymond George Hart, who first gave us his introductory lecture on RDF secrets way back at Yatesbury Radio School. I was flattered to find that he remembered me making my choice to get well versed with the AI RDF Interception Device.

From the time of my arrival at the Air Ministry I was certainly to have a time-consuming and interesting job looking after the air interception programme which was to be given the utmost urgency. Wing/Cdr. Gilbart-Smith in the Director General of Signals Department introduced me to Air Commodore Colin Peter Brown, the Director of Radar; a lanky officer who made me feel at home in the Directorate. He possessed a natural charm one seldom meets. Finally, on the rounds, we came to the office of the big man, the Director General of Signals, Air Marshal Sir Victor Tait. He gave me a warm welcome with a smile. I noticed he had a slight Canadian accent. I soon discovered that Gilfillan, the first radar officer I met during my stay with 604 Squadron at Middle Wallop, had an office only a few feet away from mine! He was now a Squadron Leader and had the new H2S centimetric radar device on his plate and his main concern was directly linked with Bomber Command. There was still a third Squadron Leader, one Rickard, in charge of ASV who cared for RAF Coastal Command requirements, viz air to surface detection of enemy vessels and submarines. I thought of the three of us as the Three Musketeers! We had regular meetings co-ordinating our work with Wing/ Cdr. Gilbart-Smith. Policy discussions were initiated and most of our information was passed by minutes to the Director. Likewise there was a very strong liaison directly with the Ministry of Aircraft Production. Our air staff requests were communicated to the Controller of Communication, then Sir Robert Renwick.

To keep pace with the ever-changing RAF priorities there was a never-ending stream of minutes originating from the two Commands. There had to be action by all concerned. The Ministry of Aircraft Production and its counterparts at TRE worked frantically. One had to remember some planning was afoot by others in readiness for a probable invasion under the code-name 'Overlord'. I should add at this juncture that nearly all radar devices had been, or were being, converted to the microwave band. A new form of AI, possessing a TV type scan on a cathode-ray tube display, was in the pipeline. Special high-power scientific meetings, usually attended by operational research and intelligence persons, were frequently held and TRE Scientists and Dr R.V. Jones (Intelligence) often came too. We were told latest news of what the enemy was up to — for example, if one of our bombers, equipped with its H2S, had fallen into enemy hands all present would naturally wish to know whether the enemy had got hold of our precious Magnetron.

Apart from general administration and attending meetings, there were numerous outside visits, frequently to experimental and research establishments, TRE, and other Command Headquarters. We had a communication flight at Hendon airfield, within easy reach from Whitehall. On one occasion I flew with Group Captain Hart. Then we were visiting an aircraft manufacturer in connection with a radar interception installation. By having such a meeting one gained much food for thought and action. Charged with the facts I could 'get cracking' whilst chairborne! Often I found it helpful to motor to Defford for a meeting and flight testing an aircraft already fitted with a special device. Later on I was able to go on to TRE at Malvern to talk over problems with a senior scientist who was responsible for a particular project. My main contact was J. A. Radcliff. I found his profound knowledge of microwave developments in the AI field very stimulating. I would add here that I felt so pleased to know such an eminent man.

On the 12th May 1942 I had the morning off from the Air Ministry to enable me to attend an Investiture at Buckingham Palace. Unfortunately it was not convenient for my wife to go to the Palace. She had to go to the Maternity Hospital for a check-up. I was glad that my father and step-mother were able to attend the ceremony. When it was my turn the King said a few words when he pinned a decoration on my chest, which unfortunately I did not clearly hear amidst the soft music playing in the background.

Four days after the Investiture I was pursuing my tasks in my office when I had a telephone call from the Director, Air Commodore C.P. Brown. I hurried to see him. He had a wonderful smile on his face and I wondered what was brewing. He said, "I have to congratulate you. I have just had a telephone message from a maternity hospital with the news that your wife has given birth to a baby daughter!" I was thrilled and was given permission to go to the hospital that evening. Before too long I was able to bring my wife and new infant Rosemary back to our temporary home in Golders Green. The Cordingly family was now complete with two daughters, Juliet and Rosemary, who would be cared for by their mother with love and attention. We wondered whether the enemy would attempt to bomb the area again and I hoped that the Morrison shelter would prove to be safe for the family.

I recall one moment at that time. It was spring and we heard at the Air Ministry that Malta was having a pretty bad time, being attacked by the enemy flying Junkers 88 bombers based in Sicily. Malta had no night fighter defensive aircraft. It had been suggested at a high level meeting at the Air Ministry that we should despatch a squadron of Beaufighters equipped with AI Mk. VIII. Since the 10 cm radar was still top secret and it would therefore be very serious if an aircraft were to be lost near enemy territory, it was considered that the Beaufighters should be flown direct to Malta minus all vital radar components. Once the Beaufighters were safe in the Malta airfield the AI radar device would be installed and flight tested. This was a big undertaking and we had to find a competent radar officer to supervise such work. Flt./Lt. Willis, ex-29 Squadron, was chosen. I had the problem of discussing ways and means with him. He was a thoroughly reliable, quiet sort of person. We next had to decide how to transport the precious equipment to Malta. If sent by a surface ship there would be a big risk and finally it was agreed that we ask the Royal Navy to carry the vital parabolic reflector and transmitter and receiver components in a submarine. This scheme was accepted by Churchill as a more urgent priority than food to Malta. I made a number of visits to the Admiralty and met the Officers in Charge of Submarines. I was able to see the type of hatch or aperture in the submarine which would permit stowage of our gear. For example, it was touch and go whether our parabolic reflector and antenna, when correctly packed, would pass through a circular water-tight hatch. Fortunately a way was found to suit the submariners. Flt./Lt. Willis was to fly out in one of the Beaufighters and carry with him all technical data for servicing and installation. He was instructed about action to take should anything unforeseen happen. The planned operation was completed without a hitch and the aircraft arrived safely on the Malta airfield. Willis had a radar workshop ready to use and the top secret gear arrived after a safe journey under the sea, thanks to the Navy and all concerned. It was heartening to learn that the Beaufighters went into action successfully.

The majority of my time until the beginning of 1943 covered weeks of technical visits to establishments such as RAF Farnborough and special flight trials at FIU Ford. Similar work at Defford was of high priority on the microwave gear: a television type of scanning presentation on a cathode-ray tube. It was an outstanding development using the work of British scientists which was the ultimate in technological development at that time. The microwave was highly accurate with a common transmitter and receiver and antenna set in a parabolic reflector which was motor-driven by a mechanism to give a fine line scan. Flying with such a sophisticated device made our early AI Mk. IV look old-fashioned. The television scanned picture was produced by a very narrow beam of radiation of high resolution. The whole installation was called AI Mk. X. It was to be produced in the United States to relieve Britain's overstretched workload.

Arrangements were made by the Air Ministry Director of Radar and

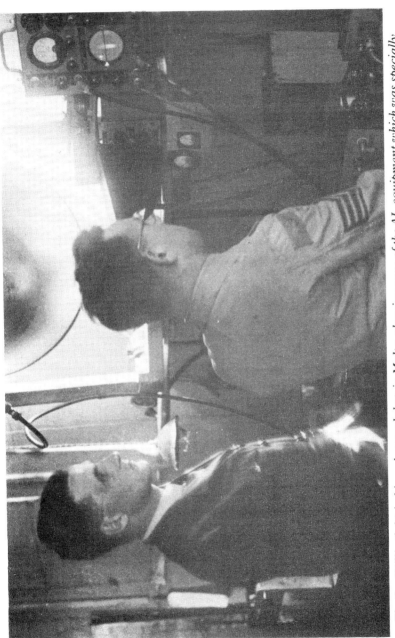

Flt./Lt. Willis (left) in his radar workshop in Malta, showing some of the AI equipment which was specially transported to the island by submarine.

the Ministry of Aircraft Production to get the new AI in the pipeline. The American Army Signals Corps planned to fit its equivalent of our new Mk. X equipment to their own night fighter aircraft 'The Black Widow' when available, and they proposed to call it SCR 720 (meaning Signal Corps Radar No. 720). There were to be mutual exchanges as to the progress of work here and in the USA. The American Western Electric Company had a contract to produce gear to meet any immediate needs and civilian engineers were to visit the UK for exchange of engineering and production designs. This called for a close-knit panel of experts to control its use and accordingly I had to see that the RAF's needs were met. With the help of the Ministry of Aircraft Production and our scientists at TRE we set up a panel to cover operational needs. There were to be some modifications to ensure that the SCR 720 would fit comfortably into the Mosquito to make it the British ultimate in the night fighter category of AI.

A special perspex bulbous nose-piece called a radome had to be designed to fit on the Mosquito nose. The all-important job was the cockpit mounting of the television scanned indication cathode-ray tube display unit and visor; the AI operator being seated to the right of the night fighter pilot.

With very high priority in mind we soon had a visit by a Western Electric Company engineer, Walter Pree, who was to spend his time with me and the Ministry of Aircraft Production. He was a good radio engineer and did all he could to make sure that our experience with the use of airborne radar on operations would be resolved. It had been arranged by the Director General of Signals that Walter Pree and I should fly to the United States on 27th March 1943 to convey the story of our own experience in combating the enemy bomber to the Americans through the auspices of the RAF delegation in Washington. I was informed that most of my work would be either in or around Washington DC and that I was likely to visit certain American establishments.

Sir Robert Watson Watt, father inventor of radar and advisor on most radar aspects, was told about my impending visit to the States. He asked to see me before I left in order to give me a briefing. Sir Robert, a short and slight man and a dour Scot, was sitting in his large upholstered armchair when I entered his office. He explained that he was anxious to know just what picture I would paint when I met our American counterparts. I assured him I would give them a brief outline of life I had shared with most squadrons using AI and the story of serviceability also was emphasized.

Mosquito aircraft showing Radome enclosing SCR 720 AI

Chapter 10

MYSTERIOUS JOURNEY

There were problems facing the Government in wartime concerning the safe movement of important personnel, and elaborate plans were made to get them to their destination without the knowledge of the enemy. I would be travelling to Washington as a civilian Government servant and I should get myself a new passport. I was photographed in an ordinary lightweight tweed suit. I was to pack my uniform in a suitcase and should carry only a lightweight overnight case. Thus equipped for the mysterious journey I joined a number of civilian types and we boarded a BOAC Albatross. It was completely 'blacked out' so we could not see out of the porthole windows.

Our first destination was Bristol where we landed, refuelled, and then took off again all very much blacked out. Eventually we landed in the Irish Free State at Shannon Airport. We were taken to a fine country club and were given an excellent lunch. We were informed that we were free to wander about the countryside and that our presence was required again for dinner. I joined some of the others and tried to guess what each did in ordinary life. One chap was obviously an American, the others were a mixed bag of Royal Navy or Army types.

It was a pleasant enough afternoon and in due time we returned to find the dinner table loaded sumptuously. The fresh salmon was delicious, and over a cup of coffee we were all told that transport would pick us up later in the evening. It turned out to be an ordinary sort of canvas-hooded vehicle and in this we all pressed on to a destination unknown to us. It was getting quite dark and we drove to a quayside with a Customs shed. The Irish officials, with a single British courier-cum-guide, looked us over and completed their papers according to the documents in hand. We had to wait until it was quite dark and then we became aware of the arrival of a fairly fast naval type launch, with searchlights and machine-guns. Once aboard, our English guide told us that we were going out to meet a Pan American Clipper flying-boat! We were far away from the land and there was a faint breeze as the searchlights picked up the giant flying-boat. The sea was pretty choppy and we had to step on the float and be hauled inside the cabin.

When we were all aboard the captain told us to take pot luck with the sleeping facilities. We would have to take turns and share bunks. There was ample food and drink so that was fine. We were told the weather forecast was fair but our destination was not mentioned. We were airborne at 21.00 and flew at a fairly good speed. Later, looking out of the starboard window, we caught a glimpse of a coastline ablaze with lights. The pilot completed a circuit, lost height and landed in the sea off the coast, which soon turned out to be Lisbon. The night was really dark and the sea still choppy. A high-speed armed craft arrived and its searchlight played on the exit door from the cabin. We were helped into the boat, still feeling sleepy; a quick turn and we were then belting along at high speed with much spray to the pier head on the shore. From there we were escorted to a cosy café where we enjoyed lashings of hot coffee served by charming Portuguese ladies. Our guide explained we would be driven to Estoril and a coach duly took us along the coast and dropped us outside a palatial hotel near the Casino. We had a snack and retired to bed in luxurious surroundings. I did not sleep well, my mind busy after all the disturbance we had had to endure. After a nice shower next morning I found my way to the dining-room and surveyed with wonder all the goodies we had been without during the war. Needless to say, I enjoyed the bacon and eggs followed by lashings of fresh fruit. After this our escort talked to us individually. He explained we would leave that night and asked us to enjoy the seaside atmosphere. We could swim or do as we wished. I had a refreshing swim then wandered back to the hotel for yet another excellent meal. We had been warned that the hotel was swarming with spies, mostly female, and naturally in the bar all of us were bereft of conversation. I enjoyed the company of Walter Pree, a good friend, whose home was in Minnesota, USA. He had a wife and children there.

Most of our party assembled for dinner. We had been asked during the morning briefing to pay special attention when the time came for us to make our exits ready for the next stage of our journey. Each person was asked to leave the dining table at a particular time and to wander off in a random fashion. We were then expected to find our way through the kitchen and assemble in the yard at the rear of the hotel where transport would be waiting. I downed my coffee and sneaked off. I followed a waiter and went through the kitchen; the Manager was in the offing and pointed to a suitable exit. The evening was warm and breezy and I walked over to a parked van. The vehicle was very full and the Manager stood on the kitchen steps as our guide bade him farewell. We moved off and as we left the Manager stood upright and gave us a Churchill 'V' sign with two fingers. Our progress was fairly slow along a winding road. We stopped by a quayside and passed through what appeared to be a Customs shed. The salty sea air stimulated my nostrils. There being no black-out in Lisbon we were able to see our speeding motor launch manoeuvring along the quayside. We all stepped in and with full speed went out to board our moored flying-boat. There was a thundering roar of four engines as the Clipper moved slowly ready for take-off. Then, on full throttle the floats lifted above the crest of the waves — she was airborne, and the engines soon settled down to a steady purr.

Walter Pree and I were feeling desperately tired and agreed to take it in turns to sleep in one of the bunks. The flying-boat was on course and I thought, 'Goodness only knows where we are heading for!' Time passed and I had the odd nightcap and settled down with my thoughts. I remembered hearing someone saying that the Luftwaffe had a Junkers 88 patrol off the coast and had already caused losses to our aircraft. It seemed ages since we were airborne. I had had a quick 'kip' in a bunk and was sitting in the cabin. The night sky was becoming lighter and eventually the sun made its presence clear with a pinkish light. It was obvious that we were travelling south and a distant coastline could be discerned through a portside window. We were travelling down the coast of West Africa and when the sun was high we landed at Boloma in Portuguese New Guinea. By Jove! It was hot. I was in need of tropical kit which I had not brought. We came ashore and our party settled in a quiet hotel already serving breakfast. I was accosted by a grubby local native trying to sell a handful of raw chicken breasts: all very unhygienic!

The Clipper was being refuelled and so we had plenty of time. I joined my travelling companions for breakfast. We were sitting on white slatted benches and there was a table-cloth gleaming white in the morning sunshine. The breakfast was out of this world; bacon with fresh mangoes and coffee. I could see that if we were to travel or exist in such tropical weather conditions I would have to do something to shed my civilian tweed suit.

Airborne again, we continued down the West Coast of Africa. A distance of some 500 miles slipped away and the Clipper prepared to land off the coast of Monrovia in Liberia. Our actual mooring was at a place called Fisherman's Lake. Here the sea was relatively calm and the Clipper taxied towards the coastal area already prepared for its anchorage and refuelling. There were a number of American service personnel present. We taxied to the end of a pontoon pier constructed from wooden planks lashed to floating empty oil drums. We were soon able to cross this pontoon pier and were greeted by the Americans in charge of this improvised air base-cum-refuelling depot for Pan American Airways. They were well organized and had all the modern comforts laid on. We were fed from tins and there were plenty of places to get a shower, for which we were all thankful. I afterwards donned some cotton pyjamas. Goodness knows what an awful tramp I looked but I was thankful to have a change from my hot suit. I spent the rest of my time at Fisherman's Lake resting while cooling off. The humidity must have been 100% and the temperature in the 90s Fahrenheit. Of course, we were actually 5° N of the Equator. At 11 o'clock on the night of 29th April 1943 the Clipper took off. The weather report was not good. We were told it would be very bumpy due to the presence of cumulus-nimbus clouds and there was the promise of thunderstorms *en route*.

We all slept spasmodically during that really bumpy and seemingly endless flight. After twelve hours flying time we sighted land in the morning light and the Clipper landed on the sea a short distance from the coast. We had arrived at Natal in Brazil. After a short wait the Brazilian launch arrived with a number of officials who swarmed into our Clipper. They said we were not to move and we had to stay put while a uniformed fellow started to fumigate the entire area. We were almost asphyxiated. One chap had a magnifying glass and a pair of tweezers. He was looking for the odd mosquito, and after our fumigation ordeal we were told that the authorities would fine Pan American Airways £5 for every insect found in the aircraft! I thought this rather a tall story and wondered whether it could be true. We were at last allowed to leave the Clipper in the launch which dumped us on the quayside. We had to assemble in a compound with a number of buildings for immigration and a medical centre. In the latter we were all checked over and a number of tests were made. The climate was hot and very humid. Our transport took us to a United States Army Air Force transit camp where nearly all the accommodation was under canvas. I had a splendid tent and there was plenty of room to stow away my possessions. Feeding facilities were available in a separate building. The camp site was dusty and looked as if it had been a sandy desert area. Parnamirim, a USAAF airfield, was not far from the camp. Next day (1st May 1943) we were airborne again, this time flying in a United States Army Air Force Boeing strato-cruiser C.75. The aircrew were very friendly and helpful. We were flying in a north-easterly direction along the coast of South America; and there were thunder storms *en route*. The dense clouds saturated with heavy rain made visibility almost nil. The pilot had to lose height in order to see the coastline to help navigation by the use of maps. Even at low altitude we could see very little through the rain. Added to this, the radio operator announced that his radio had failed so we had to press on by using maps. Since leaving Brazil we had covered 1,000 miles and looking down on the coast one could see a change in the colour of the sea. Near the coast it was a muddy yellowish brown colour. This was, of course, the coastal area around the mouth of the River Amazon. We continued flying, hugging the coastline, with the radio still out of action, and the pilot decided to make a forced landing on a jungle airstrip a few miles inland from Georgetown, the area being part of Belem, latitude 2°S, with the Amazon jungle close by. It was just as hot and humid as the climate we had left behind in Fisherman's Lake in East Africa.

The radio communications at the airstrip station were helpful and the pilot told us he hoped a relief strato-cruiser with a serviceable radio would be available soon; we should stay put till then. The humidity was unbearable and the pilot soon realized that his passengers, mostly VIPs, were still in civilian clothes and were not keen to sweat it out while waiting for another aeroplane. He was able to change his flight plans and we took off from that humid jungle strip for a short flight to Atkinson airfield, near Georgetown. The rain had stopped and it was now a waiting game. We hoped to get away in another aircraft the next day. We were all a little travel worn and were such long-suffering persons!

To our great relief the long-waited strato-cruiser airliner arrived in the morning and we were soon airborne. The violent stormy weather in the vicinity had vanished. We passed Trinidad on the port side and soon the Windward Islands and the Leeward Islands were directly below our flight path. After covering a distance of over 1,000 miles we landed at Bonenquin airfield in Puerto Rico. Life in that pleasant island was enjoyable. For the first time since we had been in transit I was able to have a good night's sleep. We were away the next morning flying in an Eastern Airlines DC3. It was the last stage of our mysterious journey. All the scattered islands in our path below flashed by, so to speak! Having covered yet another 1,000 miles plus, we all had a good view of Uncle Sam's territory before landing at Miami on 2nd April 1943 at 13.00 hours. All we pseudo 'civilians' were cleared and were pleased to be safely escorted to the adjoining Miami hotel. Walter Pree, my Western Electric Company travelling companion, was cheered with the prospect of soon being back on his home ground. One of our travelling hosts called us all together and said that our suitcases would be delivered to the hotel rooms allocated to us. We should change into our proper uniforms after resting and we should all assemble together for dinner. A quick shower and a rest was a welcome climax to our long and exhausting journey. My uniform, although a little creased, had travelled well. I went down to the hotel lounge only to find a transformation scene was working, the incongruous mixed bag of 'civilians' appearing like newly hatched butterflies! A fair sprinkling of British service people, a colonel or two, and some civil servants I would guess. Conversation at dinner-time was indeed lively. We all agreed the worst part of our journey was when we were nearly suffocated by the Brazilians with the mosquito spray in the hot and humid Clipper cabin.

Chapter 11

MISSION IN THE USA

Most of the travellers were to fetch up in Washington and that is where I was also destined to go. The next day I bade Walter Pree goodbye, arranging to meet him later in New York. An RAF colleague and I were then invited to stay with a local RAF Group Captain Liaison Chief who had a very comfortable home near Lake Okeechobee. I accepted the kind offer and we drove off through sub-tropical countryside, everywhere the trees were festooned with growths of Spanish moss hanging from their branches. The moss is, of course, a parasite. The house where we went to stay had a lovely sub-tropical garden with a deep pool set off by overlapping foliage and ferns. There were a few baby crocodiles swimming in the pool! The Group Captain had a private cabana on the beach — I was given the key and was able to swim in the Atlantic from Palm Beach. The next day I flew to Washington and stayed at the Mayflower Hotel, already frequented by British service personnel. Arrangements had been made to start the first phase of our talk with our American colleagues, US Army Signal Corps, at the Pentagon Building, the equivalent of our present Ministry of Defence. The building's design was certainly impressive. I had to check in with the security department who gave me an all-clear when I had produced my brief-case stuffed with documents. Our conference was chaired by a senior colonel. We were to exchange details of our experience in the RAF when combating the German bombers with our airborne AI interception devices. I described this during my introductory talk. Of course, our American counterparts were lacking in knowledge of how we in the RAF had been coping with the enemy bombers and I am sure they found the description of interest. Half-way through our deliberations the Chairman said, "Gentlemen! What about a coke?" He passed on a message: he then tossed a dime onto the centre of the conference table and other chaps followed him. A mobile Coke seller with a cool-box on a tricycle entered and served us with refreshing drinks. When he had checked the dimes he departed and talks, which had been going well, continued.

The main emphasis concerned engineering aspects and the need to get our new AI device into production quickly in order to keep the UK well supplied with equipment to a specification still to be debated. The SCR 720 was destined for the Mosquito. Henceforth the project would be chased by the Ministry of Aircraft Production and officers of the RAF delegation HQ under the command of Air Vice-Marshal Laing. Dr Touch, a scientific officer, acted in liaison with the HQ personnel and our American friends. We were to have numerous meetings concerning the project. One would be in New York and another at the Massachusetts Institute of Technology.

After dinner one evening I stepped out of the Mayflower. It had been typical Washington weather, hot and humid. The pavement reflected upwards its stored heat from the sun. I joined one of my colleagues and we walked to a popular place called The Old King Cole. There one could hear the talented voice of Peggy Lee who sat on top of a grand piano, swinging a leg and singing popular songs. The place was fairly full and I met several Senators and US Government officials.

A day or so later I left Washington for a brief visit to New York where I was to stay at the New Yorker Hotel. On arrival in New York I caught a taxi and suddenly an ear-splitting siren started. The taxi stopped and the driver got out. He asked me to leave and to take shelter because there was an air raid warning exercise. He suggested I proceed to the shelter in Grand Central Station. It had a lofty roof above which towered the Commodore Hotel. All pedestrians and car owners in the area had to take shelter and soon there was a milling throng of people, some slightly panicky and others not knowing what to do. I must admit I thought of the chaotic state of affairs that would arise if a sizeable bomb were to fall at the base of the surrounding skyscrapers. The all-clear signal sounded at last and I went on my way to the New Yorker Hotel. Later on I heard that this air raid practice was organized to permit the *Queen Mary* to slip out of her berth and to be well on her way heading for the Atlantic with her precious cargo. The general pandemonium undoubtedly diverted attention from this.

Walter Pree was in town so I rang him and we met in an apartment owned by a Western Electric senior engineer. We made plans for a meeting at the Bell Telephone Company premises in Whippany. The next day we all foregathered and had a lively discussion concerning changes and small improvements we wished to have incorporated in the new device SCR 720 ear-marked for the RAF. Walter Pree and I later went to Cleveland, Ohio, where we were scheduled to fly in the new

American night fighter called The Black Widow which had been fitted with the SCR 720 AI. I had an opportunity to test the equipment in flight and found it to be operationally acceptable. I thought the visor fitting to be too stiff as this might cause injury to the face if one landed heavily. Our test took place on Wright Field. After this I was back with the RAF delegation in Washington. Our next trip was to Boston, for talks at the Massachusetts Institute of Technology (MIT). Rory was there and he delivered a lively talk before the assembled company of personnel interested in AI night fighter trials in the UK. Professor Allee was our host and he welcomed our efforts to report vital information to all present. I found the MIT personnel were all sympathetic, and grateful to have our information.

After our meeting Professor Allee invited a colleague and me to dinner. We drove back from MIT with him to his abode. In the evening we went for a walk. This was intentional because the Professor wanted to exercise his tame brown bear! He armed me with a bag of raisins and lifted the latch to open the door of the bear's cage. I was 5 ft 11 ins and the bear was very nearly as tall as me. It had a restraining chain round its neck and bounded like a child. The bear suddenly saw the bag of raisins I had in my hand. It stood up on its hind legs and grasped me in a genuine bear hug! The Professor took the bag of raisins from me and the beast then let go and went to enjoy the titbits. We all walked through a lovely wooded area; every now and then the bear would make a dash towards a sapling tree and climb it until it bent downwards almost double.

Having had good exercise and an enjoyable meal I was driven back to the MIT car-park. On entry we were challenged by a Negro guard. The Professor stopped and exchanged a few words. He told us a true story which had happened at that very car-park. Apparently the Professor used to go to his laboratory late in the evening and it was his custom to carry a revolver in a holster held by a strap round his waist. On one particular evening he was challenged and as he leaned forward from the driving seat to answer, the revolver slipped out of its holster. In the darkness the guard saw the moving revolver and thought the Professor was about to use it on him, so he immediately fired his own gun and the bullet passed through the Professor's stomach. He, poor fellow, then had a bad time being patched up by the hospital. He was fighting fit when I met him and just wanted to let us know how 'quick on the draw' the security guards were when challenging anyone who entered the MIT car-park.

When our first conference came to an end I went to Quancet in Rhode Island. I had been invited by the US Navy to visit the HQ there. I was to fly with Lt. Abercrombie in a Beechcraft and test their AIA interception equipment. We were flying under the control of their GCI. I was duly impressed with the remarkably fine picture of high resolution, both with the airborne device and the ground station. They had a really excellent PPI indicator picture of Cape Cod. After the flight trials I was able to enjoy their hospitality and to sample the local seafood. It was my first taste of clam chowder and it was jolly good. A US Army Signals Corps colonel, who had been present at the conference, afterwards tackled me and asked whether I could visit Boca Raton Training Establishment near Orlando in order to give a lecture to the trainees. I checked my programme and agreed that I could fit it in, but I was not sure about transport as it was a long way south of Miami. He said it was only a 1,300 mile trip and he would organize a Navy pilot to fly me down the East Coast so that I would arrive in good time to meet the assembled company at the USAAF Staff Training College. We fixed up the visit for 29th May, and meanwhile I stayed on in Boston to write up my report on our meetings. One evening while I was dining alone at the Statler Hotel in Boston I experienced a typical gesture of American hospitality. Not far from my dining table was an American with his wife and daughter. They were enjoying a meal together and realized from my RAF squadron leader's uniform that I was alone and away from home. The father came over, apologized for intruding and asked if I would like to share their table. This was indeed a very friendly offer which I happily accepted. They were typical New England Bostonians. We had an enjoyable meal and talked about England and wartime conditions. The little orchestra that had been playing quietly suddenly struck up a dance tune. I asked the daughter if she would care to dance and off we went. When we returned to our table I felt I had done the right thing and having spent a very enjoyable evening with a thoroughly good dinner, I bade the family good-night and retired to bed.

On 29th May 1943 I was ready for my flight south down the East Coast of America to fulfil the invitation to lecture to the USAAF trainees at Boca Raton. A single engined aircraft with a noisy radial engine was ready for me at Quancet. The pilot, a naval lieutenant, came up to me. We discussed our route and he told me we would have to make a number of stops to refuel. We took off about 10 a.m. We were able to converse using the plane's intercom. We were to fly straight down the East Coast and our first stopping place was to be La Guardia, New York. The clustered New England dwellings, white-painted and timber-clad, shone bright in the morning sunlight. We hugged the coastline and 100 miles passed. We would shortly be seeing New York. Sure enough the tall buildings and skyscrapers were soon perilously close as the pilot suddenly said, "Do you want to see the Empire State Building?" already clearly visible. The pilot was preparing to land at La Guardia Airport when the air traffic controller radioed to say that air traffic regulations had been infringed as the pilot had flown too close to a built up area and he must report after refuelling. I said I hoped he would not get into trouble on my account. After refuelling he had to report his reason for being close to the city boundary. The pilot told them that he was in a hurry and was transporting a VIP to Miami. I chuckled and thought the excuse was apt. We flew on and I was able to get an excellent view of the east coastline of America. Eventually we came to the Florida coast and shortly afterwards we flew over Boca Raton and could see the huge parade ground and the buildings. While the pilot orbited the parade ground area a radio controller piped up to the effect, "Get the hell out of it!" Apparently the noise of the engine was upsetting an address being given to the assembly on the parade ground. Forthwith the pilot replied, "Sorry! I've got a VIP aboard who is a guest of the Commander." My pilot did a circuit and proceeded to land at Orlando Airfield. When eventually we taxied up to a dispersal point we were met by a large staff-car bearing a star-spangled pennant! The commanding officer of the training centre greeted me and cracked a joke about the noisy aircraft. He entertained me to dinner and later that evening we set off to the training centre building. It was already full of chaps. After a formal introduction I was handed over to the lecture desk. The theme of my address was how England was defended against the German bombers by night fighters equipped with airborne radar interception devices — their performance, technical snags and serviceability. I talked for a while and the hushed attention told me everything was going well. We had a break for questions and, believe me, I was kept busy answering a bombardment of them, during which I suddenly became aware of a long line of glasses of beer gradually creeping their way towards the lecture desk! I was somewhat overwhelmed and knew I simply could not cope with such a volume so I had a couple as a token gesture and called a stop. We started up again with the next part of my talk and eventually I was feeling I ought to finish. The chairman agreed that we should stop after a few more minutes for questions. Finally I had to offer them my thanks and to pack up. Thus ended a long, fairly full but successful day, and I slept well that night.

The next day I was back in Washington DC with the RAF Delegation HQ. Plans were already afoot to consider how the completed SCR 720 AI sets were to be transported when ready for despatch to the UK. They were urgently wanted for installation and flight testing on our Mosquitoes. There were two modes of transport which we considered safe: transit free from enemy interference was all important. The methods were discussed with the RAF Delegation Chief. Could a space be allocated in the *Queen Mary*? The idea seemed fairly sound and it was agreed that the decision be put to Churchill.

Chapter 12

ATLANTIC FLIGHT HOMEWARD

I had left the UK for my long flight to Washington at the end of April. It was now mid-June and high summer. I had had a pretty tight programme and had, so far, fulfilled most of my commitments. I was still to visit Canada and to go to the Royal Canadian Air Force Radio School at Clinton. Here a number of radio officers were trained in the latest radar techniques. I fixed my return journey to the UK with my colleagues at RAF delegation. It was fortunate that I had a date to visit the RCAF Radio School as it enabled me to return to the UK with a few of the 'first off' productions of SCR 720 equipment which would be loaded on to a Liberator at Dorval. Thus everything seemed to dovetail into the plan. I felt a little sad at leaving Washington: a very well planned city with its busy Potomac River. On 12th June I said goodbye to my friends at the HQ and flew by DC3 to Detroit and then to Windsor, Ontario. Here I changed planes and flew in a TCA Hudson to Clinton, where I visited the Radio School. I had a very friendly reception and was indeed surprised to see my good friend Flt./Lt. Martin, who was my tutor at Yatesbury where he gave me so much of his time at the Radio School in 1942. The training syllabus was comprehensive and there were quite a number of RCAF trainees in the pipeline. That night I stayed at the Windsor Hotel in Montreal. The evening was very warm with a summer freshness in the air. I was able to go to the top of Mount Royal and to relax and enjoy listening to a Beethoven concert played by a symphony orchestra. As the sun dipped in the western sky the evening darkness enshrouded me and I was surrounded by hundreds of fireflies, darting about in the warm evening air. After an evening of glorious music I returned, refreshed, to my hotel.

The next morning I went straight to Dorval only to find my colleague Wing/Cdr. Rory Chisholm present. We were to fly the Atlantic together on our return journey to the UK. Our Liberator pilot was a Captain McVicar. He was the First Pilot and Rory was to fly as Second Pilot. Our precious SCR 720 equipment was already loaded in the aircraft. We were airborne at 09.25 hours and flew to Gander in

86

Newfoundland. We were to fly on the Great Circle route direct to Prestwick in Scotland.

After a delay in Gander we were off over the Atlantic with a forecast of fair weather ahead of us. I acted as an aircrew member and operated the ASV radar equipment. Periodically I looked at the ASV CRT and was able to see echoes from surface vessels and report their presence. We were pressing on at a fairly good rate. After nearly ten hours flying we eventually landed at Prestwick. It had been an uneventful crossing in calm weather.

Having disembarked I went to see the station commander and asked for an armed guard to be placed by the Liberator, explaining that it contained highly secret equipment in stowage, and that the Air Ministry would give instructions for the removal and safe transport of our radar as soon as possible.

On my return to London I was happy to find all was well with my family. I was able to hand over a bag of citrus fruit which I purchased before leaving Montreal. Lemons were a rarity in those days! The garden in my temporary home at Golders Green looked flourishing and it was good to feel I was home and well away from the hectic pace of life across the Atlantic. Arrangements were soon made to get the SCR 720 out of the Liberator on the tarmac at Prestwick and we expected soon to have a Mosquito ready for flight trials.

Periodic high-power meetings were held at Telecommunications Research Establishment, Malvern and many senior Air Ministry staff and TRE scientists attended to assess the air warfare situation and scientific progress. Such meetings, called and chaired by Mr Rowe, the Superintendent at TRE, were known as 'The Sunday Soviet'. On my return from America I attended one and was able to report on my work in Washington. On this occasion J.A. Radcliff and Dr Cockburn were present.

It was my usual habit to walk up Whitehall in my lunch hour and to eat a snack at the National Gallery. One day I was lucky to find Myra Hess at the piano giving one of her lunch-time concerts. I sat on the stone step in the entrance hall and enjoyed a sandwich while Myra played J.S. Bach's 'Jesu Joy of Man's Desiring'. Sometimes for a change I went to the Queen Elizabeth's Officers' Club at the top of Whitehall on the right; it was an excellent place to feed. There were times when many of us in the Directorate used to walk through St James's Park and patronize another Officers' Luncheon Club in Piccadilly. Mental and physical relaxation were all we needed before becoming chairborne.

In 1943 the dreary wartime atmosphere was still present. Enemy air activity had quietened and considerable activity was going on behind the scenes here in the UK. A great deal of work was being undertaken in preparation for our ultimate trials with the new AI. Bomber Command had its hands full. I found a full work load waiting for me after my comprehensive work in and around the USA and things were fairly hectic. Eventually I was able to take a break for some leave with my family. We went away early in July, first to the family home in Coleshill of my wife's father; two of his sisters lived there in a charming cottage. Here we were away from the madding crowd, and we really let the country life take over and envelop our lives. My two daughters were growing fast and their boundless energy was a joy to behold. The second half of my leave took us to the West Country where we were able to stay with Mary, my brother Eric's wife. He was still absent from home while suffering the indignities of being a prisoner of war in Japanese hands — he was working on the Burma railroad. Our two daughters were happy playing with my brother's two small boys in the large Rectory at Leckhampton. We had a beautiful summer that year and I was refreshed and soon back at Whitehall.

Early in August the RAF started to drop metal foil strips, code-named 'Window', from aircraft to form a cloud of reflecting elements which upset the radio echo. This played havoc with the German radar ground stations. It was difficult for the enemy to judge the numbers of aircraft in the darkness. On 12th August 1943 the *Daily Telegraph* reported 'RAF planes raiding Turin on Saturday dropped a special device giving out electro-magnetic rays which disturbed the Italian radio detectors.' The strips were black on one side and silver on the other. It is interesting that in February 1944 the Luftwaffe started to drop metal foil strips, very similar to ours in design. I even found a blackbird's nest being constructed with a mixture of grasses and metal foil woven together! This was early in the spring of that year.

In October, at the Fighter Interception Unit at Ford, I had my first flight in a Mosquito fitted with one of the prototypes of SCR 720. We flew at an altitude of 10,000 feet and used a Beaufighter as a target. It was detected at a range of 5 miles and I was able to see the position and height of the incoming echo. A high resolution picture on the TV-type screen was present and I thought it was good. At last the great day for final tests arrived. On 2nd November 1943 we had a Wellington II specially equipped with SCR 720 to be used as a flying class-room. We had a number of passengers: Wing/Cdr. George Adams (in charge of

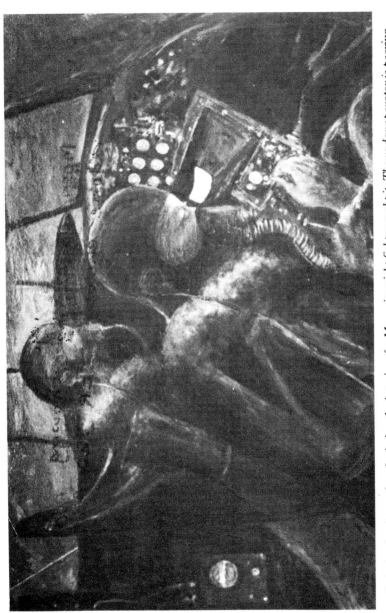

Painting by the author depicting the interior of a Mosquito night fighter cockpit. The radar operator is peering into the SCR 720 cathode ray tube indicator unit.

radar at Fighter Command), and two Australian signals officers whom I had already met in Washington DC. All went well and the flying class-room was an ideal place in which to observe the general performance of the new interception device.

We hoped to have a combined meeting with FIU, TRE and other interested parties at the Air Ministry. The need for a special meeting was long overdue and the Controller of Communications, Sir Robert Renwick, took the chair. It was a big meeting with members from the Ministry of Aircraft Production and TRE scientists. The programme on which future planning decisions were to be made was settled to our satisfaction including Fighter Command. There were decisions to be made regarding the future employment of radar-equipped Mosquitoes to be used as intruders operating over enemy territory. Also they were to be considered for use as escorts for Bomber Command when there was a likelihood of German night fighter interference. We also had heard through our intelligence source that Germany's Luftwaffe was really concerned with the Mosquito tactics or presence over its territory. I think I heard a rumour to the effect that a German destroying a Mosquito would have an extra bonus of an Iron Cross.

In late autumn we were disturbed to see from intelligence reports at the Air Ministry that the enemy was preparing to bombard London with a pilotless, engine-driven rocket called the V1. In October 1943 we also heard of the existence of a larger rocket with a range to destroy London. Bomber Command had bombed Peenemunde where the rockets were made and tested. The Cabinet and Air Ministry were concerned because there was no easy way to intercept and destroy them. At least there existed an American anti-aircraft shell fitted with a proximity fuse. The whole matter still had to be resolved. I came to the conclusion that it would probably be unsafe for my family to stay on in our temporary home and we started to make plans for them to go to my sister-in-law's family in Scotland. According to intelligence reports filtering through, the German rocket blitz was scheduled to start in 1944. In fact the first attack with V2 rockets started in June 1944.

Towards the end of 1943, I heard I was to move again. One morning in December I was summoned to the Director of Radar's office. Pacing up and down his office carpet with thumbs in his breast pockets was Air Vice-Marshal Addison. He was smoking a small cigar and he did not speak immediately. The Director said I was to be posted to a new group still to be formed. It was to be No. 100 (Bomber Support) Group for special duties under Bomber Command. I was told that my experience and special knowledge of airborne radar for destroying enemy bombers was considered useful. Air Vice-Marshal Addison said a few kind words to the effect that he would be glad to have me and that I should report to him at the new HQ. He told me the new group would be mainly concerned with radio countermeasures. I thanked my new chief, returned to my office and pulled out a map. As I sat and thought I realized that this move would fit in very well with my plan to move my family to Scotland. I would soon be living in the Officers' Mess and would not have to travel every day to London. I had also received notification that I had been promoted to Wing Commander.

*Flying class-room — Wellington aircraft equipped to take the new AI Mk. X
(SCR 720). The Mosquito scanner radome replaces the gun turret on the nose.
The actual radar was one of the first consignment received in the UK.
(Crown copyright photograph)*

Chapter 13

RADIO COUNTERMEASURES AT 100 (BOMBER SUPPORT) GROUP

On the appointed date in the New Year, and with the family already safely in Scotland, I set forth by car to West Raynham. It was a fairly long drive through the Norfolk countryside. A wintry cold wind was blowing but I made good progress and arrived in plenty of time. West Raynham was a well-established station. It was the third airfield I was to stay at since Yatesbury. HQ No. 100 (Bomber Support) Group was to use the station as its temporary headquarters whilst being formed. Afterwards it was to move to occupy a new HQ at an old country mansion in Dereham. The special duties aspect of the Group were of great importance and were of a 'hush-hush' category. Our main task would involve the use of radio countermeasures employing spoof tactics and the use of tricks to confuse the Luftwaffe operations. In point of fact it was an extension of the work in which the AVM Addison had been engaged and it was, I gathered, the work of a specialist and dear to his heart. I reported to him on arrival. He was pleased to see me and said he had a big problem to be solved which concerned the Mosquito aircraft. We went to examine the Mosquito and he explained that the squadron had been grounded for weeks. They had difficulty in getting the special antennas to work properly in flight. The device used for countermeasures depended upon the use of metal foil which had to be kept in good contact with the leading edges of the aircraft's wooden wings. In flight the foil tended to lift and a good adhesive was therefore required to fix this. I walked back with the AOC and discussed the job. We were joined by the new Chief Signals Officer, Sam Goodman. I said I thought a watertight adhesive ought to be used to fix the metal foil. The AOC picked up a copy of *Flight* magazine and said, "Why not call in the Bostik man?" — an expression already in print as part of that company's advertisement. I telephoned the Bostik company the next morning requesting they should send a man to discuss our problem and I offered to put their representative up for the night. Lo and behold, a man dressed in a natty suit arrived in the evening. His car was loaded with all kinds of Bostik products including a suitcase full of samples for convenient handling during discussions. I escorted him to his room where he left the case of samples. I have hesitated to tell the story of the 'Bostik Man' but I feel it illustrates the kind of situation which might happen any time in similar circumstances. In this case the aircrew were restless because their aircraft had been grounded for weeks. Well, I entertained the Bostik man to dinner in the Mess and afterwards we went to the bar for the odd beer. There were a few pilots and radar observers already present so I introduced them to my guest and explained I hoped he would help us to get them airborne soon! The chaps were told we hoped to find a suitable adhesive to stick the metal foil on the Mosquito wing leading edges. I am afraid some aircrew members had been lapping up the beer and they challenged the Bostik man, saying they doubted his product would do the job. He, being a good sales engineer, said that if they did not believe him he would get his case and show them his products. They thought this a good idea so he went to his room and returned with the case of samples. From then onwards the trouble started. The Bostik man picked up a squeezable tube of black compound and said he was sure it would do the job. I insisted we ought not to jump to any conclusions and we should wait until the morning. A youngish pilot took the tube and gave it a squeeze. A big blob of black adhesive appeared. At this point I regret to say the situation developed into a riot. The aircrew members grabbed the tubes and started to stick a chap's ears back, covering his hair with black sticky compound. Other experiments were afoot and everyone started to remove samples from the case. I tried to stop one pilot from sticking the Bostik man's pockets together and found he had already glued the lapels. On the floor behind me someone was rolling a chap up in a carpet and trying to seal up the overlapped ends. I hoped a squadron flight commander would come in to help restore order and in the meantime tried to stop the beer drinking which was half the cause of the trouble. I was suddenly aware of the action in the ante-room. Someone had taken a shield with antlers attached from the wall and was trying to stick the shield to the glass panel of the entrance door. The poor Bostik man was by now very worried, his suit was stuck together, and the chap who had had his ears stuck back simply could not shift them. A flight commander then appeared and I explained the circumstances amidst the chaos and he helped to bundle the party off to their bedrooms with instructions that they should all attend the medical section next morning when a suitable solvent would have to be found to unstick hair and ears and to clean up. The next morning they apparently had a very difficult job in trying to do the unsticking. I was joined by Group Captain Goodman and with the Bostik man we went off to the Mosquitoes. I had to tell Sam Goodman the story. He did see the amusing side of it. Needless to say we did find a suitable waterproof adhesive to fix the metal strips and in the end most of our sticky problems of the past evening were glossed over and we were soon ready for flight trials with the respective antennas in situ. I was sharing an office with Wing/Cdr. McMenemy and he too enjoyed the Bostik story. Later in the morning I looked for the antlers which had been stuck to the glass door panel. Somehow they had been carefully removed. I thought over the aircrew's behaviour the night before. In the circumstances there was an understandable reason why they gave vent to their feelings. I was indeed sorry for the Bostik man who put up a good show. Certainly his adhesive products solved our problem.

After our short stay at West Raynham the group moved to its new permanent home at Bylaugh Hall, Dereham. It was an oldish building: a country house which was substantial looking in grey stone. The grounds had been neglected though some attempt had been made to keep the weeds down in places. Where there were lovely trees like silver birches and flowering cherries the weeds had taken over. A long drive led up the entrance of the house. Patches of heather and lily of the valley grew under shrubs and bushes: there were wild birds in that environment too. Iron railings ringed the front of the house which had an imposing entrance accessible from a flight of stone steps. The entrance hall floor was paved with a smooth stone of marble-like surface and an elegant stone staircase went up to the first floor where I had an office facing the garden at the rear of the house. It had a view of lawn and shrubs. Wing/Cdr. McMenemy shared my office and next door to us was accommodation for the Chief Signals Officer, Group Captain Sam Goodman. On the first floor front were the offices of Air Vice-Marshal Addison, our AOC, and also an office belonging to Rory Chisholm who was then an Air Commodore and Senior Air Staff Officer: Dunning-White and Ken Davidson, both Wing Commanders, were situated next to Rory. Also located in the building was an intelligence office with Wing/Cdr. 'Sunshine' Wells in charge. I was pleased to find Dr Leonard Lamerton, a scientific officer, in charge of operational research. I had first met him in my civilian job as an X-ray engineer, at the British Institute of Radiology. At that time he was concerned with cancer research. Thus our interests were in X-rays. Of course, he was invariably busy in 100 Group doing some sort of statistical work relating to the operational performance of our squadrons and our AI

100 (Bomber Support) Group HQ Signals Staff: (centre row, 6th from left) Wing/Cdr. W. McMenemy; (front row 2nd from left) SASO Air Commodore R. E. R. Chisholm, CBE, DSO, DFC; (3rd left) AOC Air Vice-Marshal E. B. Addison, CB, CBE; (4th left) CSO Group Captain S. Goodman, CBE; (extreme right) the author, Wing/Cdr. N. C. Cordingly, OBE.

interception devices. Adjacent to Bylaugh Hall were separate buildings housing teleprinters and the cipher personnel who were mainly WAAF officers. We had an Officers' Mess of reasonable size within easy walking distance from the hall. Most officers were housed in their own Nissen huts with curved roofs. These were sited below trees and well camouflaged. One had to trip through the undergrowth to the bath house: the water there was invariably scalding hot in the morning. The cold East Anglian wind often blew and sometimes the insulation of the Nissen huts was not very good. It was a bit difficult to get to sleep, an extra blanket helped. I parked my car at night between the Nissen hut and the tree trunks. One spring morning I happened to glance through the near side window and was entertained by a pair of spotted fly-catchers who had made a nest in a tree only a foot away from the car near side door!

Most of our night fighter airfields were within easy reach of the HQ. The squadron was by now equipped with Mosquitoes fitted with the new SCR 720 AI, as planned by the Air Ministry programme. Some airfields, North Creek for example, had a number of heavy bombers — Lancasters, Halifaxes and Stirlings. Later on the US Army Air Force occupied Sculthorpe with Flying Fortresses and Liberators. They joined us and we were all to use radio countermeasures. The Mosquito role was under review both acting as night fighters or as night intruders in Bomber Command strategy. Thus HQ 100 Group had soon become quite a complex organization, manned by specialists and men with experience, all working for the main cause and using radio countermeasures (RCM). As already stated, the US Army Air Force also had a share in the use of RCM tactics. They had ample supplies of 'Chaff' which was a form of 'Window'. The metallized strips were cut to a particular length to suit the wavelength of the enemy ground station used by the Luftwaffe for navigational aids or radio communications. In my humble opinion the new group was quite an unorthodox 'set-up', judged by pre-war standards.

On the night of 30-31st March 1944 Bomber Command made a large attack on Nuremburg. It suffered very heavy losses; out of 795 aircraft sent on the raid 94 were lost. This was certainly a great blow to Bomber Command. Sir Archibald Sinclair, Secretary of State for Air, visited 100 Group personally to show his concern. The AOC telephoned me and said he was entertaining Sir Archibald to lunch in the Mess and I was invited to join his party. Rory Chisholm and Sam Goodman were also present. During lunch the Under Secretary said to the AOC, "Where was 100 Group during the raid?" or something to that effect. I think the general feeling that we expressed was that most of our bomber losses were due to the activity of the enemy night fighters equipped with their own radar. We felt that we should send a Mosquito escort with our bombers but there were snags to this. Either we could home-on to the German night fighter aircraft's radar with a special receiver or we could interfere with enemy equipment by using a jammer transmitter. The situation was delicate and had to be resolved. We all had strong feelings about it and for a while we were writing minutes to one another. I wrote to a number of colleagues through the AOC. I received a reply which was apt. The AOC had put a footnote to this effect, 'Too much bumf, not enough action! Get cracking!' This was exactly my feeling but we still wanted a decision. The AOC's reaction was typical of his ways! He was right, we ought to have a high-power meeting. I called at his office and found him busy writing while standing at his special wall-desk. We discussed the contents of his minute, and we must now do battle with the German night fighters.

One evening when I had just dined in the Mess, I was joined by Wing/Cdr. McMenemy. As usual we were talking 'shop'. The AOC telephoned and asked us both to join him for a chat. He had his own living quarters in an ante-room on the ground floor in Bylaugh Hall. It was a comfortable apartment and we found him sitting in an armchair and wearing a sports jacket. It was nice to have a chance to get to know him — I used often to see him at the Air Ministry and thought him a bit fierce! However, meeting him that evening I found him very friendly. He was always in good form when telling stories of his early work and the various tricks he played leading up to the tactics of radio countermeasures. He told us how in the early stages of the enemy bombing attacks on us in the UK, Intelligence heard the Germans were using Ruffian beams. Knickebein beams were also used as a navigation aid to their bombers. In one system a beam was directed over the UK so that it passed, for example, over a town. A second beam intersected the first beam so that when the enemy bomber flew along the first beam it received a signal at the point of intersection which automatically dropped the bombs. A clock device was used with the system. In some cases we were able to tune in to the signal emitted by the beam and were able to jam it by using a suitable radio transmitter. The AOC also said he was able to commandeer some diathermy apparatus which was used as part of his jamming system. I expressed my interest and told him I had designed such equipment in civilian life which we used for medical therapy and sometimes for surgery. It was high frequency apparatus employing a spark-gap oscillator. That evening with our AOC host was enjoyable. We talked well past midnight over a glass or so of Scotch.

We all found while engaged in the group's numerous activities that there was a distinct need for relaxation. I simply had to have a break occasionally, even if it were only a few hours. There was nothing more enjoyable than being able to wander into the country surroundings and there to get cracking with my sketch book and water-colour paints. In springtime it was 'just the job' with a cuckoo perched on a nearby tree. There were other opportunities to get away from it all. I was fortunate enough to meet Hugh Wormold, a keen horticulturalist and ornithologist. He had a house on the fringe of Bylaugh Hall grounds and I used to have tea with Hugh and his wife. We wandered through the dense area full of trees and in this bushy wilderness we observed a school of gold crests. Later one evening we met together and were lucky enough to listen to the churring sound of the nightjars. After these breaks I returned to my office refreshed to clear my action tray. A competent WAAF sergeant stenographer was usually in attendance to help with the accumulated paperwork. She was a stickler for hard work and I have every praise for her and for the other girls who worked so hard.

Our night fighters continued to scan the night skies with their AI to engage enemy airborne radar equipped fighters. They were now taking all forms of violent evasive action; our fighters performed hair-raising aerobatic manoeuvres in order to maintain contact, they held on until their cannon shells found their mark. In this phase, just as in earlier phases, the enemy was again beaten. Our night fighters' 'bag' was almost always a good one. The heavy toll of the enemy's dwindling numbers continued into the spring of 1944 and then stopped almost completely. A period of comparative quiet reigned at home and we knew the clouds were gathering before the storm. Occasionally a small force of enemy planes came over at night to snoop and to bomb our ports where he no doubt suspected shipping was being gathered for an invasion. The whole world knew this would occur before long somewhere on the enemy occupied Continent. Needless to say the 'snoopers' and 'would-be bombers' were suitably dealt with! The quietness was not to remain for long and on the night of 5th June 1944 D-Day arrived and the Allies invaded Northern France. Sam Goodman, our CSO, invited us to see his invasion map that had been hanging on his office wall covered and locked up until now. All our Group was active and the sky hummed with bomber and fighter aircraft. We visited some personnel near by and wished them well. The Group's radio countermeasures plans were in action and so were many others from forces near the South Coast. During this hectic period everyone had a pent-up feeling and it took quite a while to become normal afterwards. From D-Day onwards the night fighters were once again busy patrolling the beach-heads and protecting the Allied landing operations. Immediately the beach-heads were occupied and the Brest Peninsula had fallen to the Allies, airfields became available for the reception of certain night fighter aircraft.

Chapter 14

THE BUZZ-BOMB THREAT AND NIGHT FIGHTERS IN THE OFFENSIVE ROLE

From D-Day onwards things started going well for the Allies on the Continent. Then the enemy launched a new form of bombing attack directed at London. They were pilotless V1 flying bombs, better known as 'buzz-bombs'. At first, in the daytime, fast single-engined fighters like the Tempest attempted to intercept and shoot down the diabolical flying bombs, with some success. We then wondered whether we could use a twin-engined Mosquito, radar-equipped, to tackle this new menace. London was suffering and the term 'buzz-bomb alley' was coined covering the bombs' flight over London's built-up area. These bombs were hurled at the great city for many months both night and day and in all weathers from bases in Northern France and Belgium. At night the buzz-bombs were intercepted by our night fighters before they could make landfall on the South Coast: those bombs that managed to pass overland were tackled by a very concentrated ack-ack barrage. Further towards the target a terrific balloon barrage was erected to net any which escaped the former measures. Thus whenever the weather permitted, our night fighters were up intercepting and destroying the enemy's much-prized reprisal weapon in large numbers. It was not many days after this new form of terror attack started that a proportion of well over 80% were destroyed by the combined effort of AI equipped night fighters, anti-aircraft guns using proximity fused shells, and the balloon barrage. Unlike the enemy night bombers, the night fighters had no difficulty seeing the fiery tail of the buzz-bomb from a long way off without using the AI secret weapon. They would have the greatest difficulty in judging the projectile's speed and distance — these factors being vital to the pilot in order to shoot and destroy. I have an interesting story to tell about an attack on a buzz-bomb. It so happened that my brother's wife had a young brother called Jim. By coincidence I discovered that Jim, a Flight Lieutenant, was a Mosquito pilot with 157 Squadron stationed at one of 100 Group's airfields at Swanington and his aircraft was one equipped with SCR 720. On one occasion he was patrolling in the vicinity of a buzz-bomb's flight path. Eventually he got a contact and gave chase after a V1 which turned out to be on a 'head-on' course. Jim fired and hit the warhead. The V1 exploded in mid-air and Jim had a 'near miss'. He flew through the flying debris and his windscreen was almost obscured by a black smutty oil film from the V1's engine. Some of the fabric was stripped away from parts of the aircraft's surfaces and the radar radome, made of perspex, cracked like an eggshell. It was fortunate that the aircraft's flying controls were not damaged and Jim returned to base and landed unscathed. I was able to inspect the Mosquito and was glad the AI was reasonably intact with the exception of the antenna portion. It was a miracle that Flt./Lt. Matthews was not killed in that operation. I made a cartoon sketch of his Mosquito afterwards.

So far I have confined myself to the night fighter used in the defensive role. There was another important role: that of the offensive night fighter. Using AI radar these were called intruders, perhaps one of the most hazardous and skilled flying operations of the war. Offensive night fighters used in support of Bomber Command operations, were stepped up to a phenomenal figure, as many as 1,000 four-engined bombers being employed in one single night against enemy targets situated several hundred miles inside Germany. It was this stage of the war's progress that the enemy started to concentrate on building up its own night fighter force which had certainly made its mark during the bombing raids already discussed. Our AI equipped Mosquitoes caused a considerable nuisance to the Luftwaffe. Certainly Goering made this evident by stepping up awards to aircrews who had tried hard but had nevertheless encountered the sting from the Mosquito! British and American bombers continued their raids on specific targets. I well remember waking up one morning in my Nissen hut and listening to the plug chain on my metal wash-basin resonating in harmony with the thunderous roar of US Flying Fortresses and Liberators forming up before setting off on a bombing mission. I got up, opened my hut door and looked up. The sky was teeming with the buzzing bombers. This was simply part of air warfare.

Our Mosquitoes continued to harass enemy territory, flying low level to strafe railways, engines and freight trains as far away as Italy.

There were several eminent specialist pilots whose names were well known for their achievements while flying as intruders in Mosquitoes. Two were Wing/Cdr. Braham and Wing/Cdr. Sammy Hoar. Sammy, who sported a handlebar moustache, was known to fly low and often complained about the accuracy of his altimeter. He even talked about operating at an altitude of 50 feet which led me to produce a cartoon sketch. Another famous character who was present on the Group HQ staff was Wing/Cdr. J.B. Tait, DSO and Bar. He was in fact a precision expert in dropping 'Tall Boys', long bombs for piercing armour plate. He was so accurate that he could drop a bomb into a barrel — it is said that one day he actually did this! He was responsible for sinking the *Tirpitz*, the large battleship which had been lying in Trondheim Fjord for a long time. Wing/Cdr. Tait, with great precision, dropped his armour-piercing bomb and got a direct hit through the deck of the battleship. From there on he was known as 'Tirpitz Tait'. He was an incredible character with a double DSO.

Another intruder pilot I specially remember for his hair-raising tactics was Micky Martin, a dare-devil Australian. One night he took off on a mission. It is alleged that he penetrated the Italian frontier, shot up an ammunition train, and on his return to base changed direction and landed at an airfield near Paris. All at HQ were concerned about his non-arrival at base. However, next day he turned up unscathed, having had a night of gay Paris in Montmartre! His next duty was to report to the AOC who probably 'tore him off a strip'. Micky was certainly a great character and was undoubtedly an excellent pilot on intruder missions.

Later in the autumn of 1944 the Germans started the V2 rocket bombardment of London. We in 100 Group went out to employ radio countermeasures to stop the launching procedure used by the enemy. It was not unusual to see a 100 Group Flying Fortress equipped as a flying laboratory, stuffed with a considerable number of Black Boxes containing radio jammers and radio devices to cause interference. Externally the Fortress bristled with all manner of antennas. The aircraft then flew near the V2 launching pads in an endeavour to interfere with any type of signal used to launch the projectile. At the time I produced another cartoon sketch of this.

Our night fighters were still regularly engaged on formidable tasks in an intruder role, disrupting the enemy night fighter operations as they attempted to destroy aircraft on airfields. This was a great asset to Bomber Command and its operations over enemy territory. We still had to resolve problems of Luftwaffe interference: this had been given a high priority. Air Ministry Intelligence had confirmed the existence of enemy radar interception equipment known as SN2 and the operational frequency of this was already known to us. The Junkers 88 aircraft were equipped with the gear. They also had a homing device called Flenzberg. I flew to Defford and also visited TRE Malvern for a conference on the fitting of tail-warning devices to Mosquitoes. Later on, we had a meeting at the Royal Aircraft Establishment at Farnborough when the JU 88 aircraft's

SN2 interception device was discussed. Here again radio counter-measures, tail-warning, and 'Homers' were reviewed.

As the year 1944 neared its end there was considerable activity to get all RCM devices into use where the frequency of enemy equipment was known. One of our Mosquitoes was lost over enemy territory. It contained one of our radio countermeasures units. As it had been reported as lost in an area already left by the retreating Germans I was instructed by the AOC to fly to France and try to get hold of the Black Box. My pilot and I flew to Jouvancourt in France. The grass airfield had been occupied by a small contingent of RAF who were housed in a collection of discarded wooden packing crates. Their only communication was a land-line to Reims. On one side of the airfield was a cluster of tallish trees each covered with a bushy growth of mistletoe. We managed to get motor transport to Reims where, in spite of enquiries, I was unable to get any sensible story about our lost equipment. We decided there was nothing for it but to return to the UK and on leaving Reims we came to a typical French farm. We stopped to talk to the two men wearing the proverbial berets and asked the way to Jouvancourt. They were kind and helpful and one man led us to a barn. He threw open the door and we noticed that the floor was covered with straw about two to three feet deep. The man called out, and, lo and behold! a trap door opened, scattering the straw and a man's head popped up! He had in his hands some bottles of champagne. We thought that this was an ideal headquarters for the French resistance movement. It transpired that because we were wearing British RAF uniform they thought we might like to take away a few bottles of champagne. They were very cheap so we bought a number and went on our way with an ideal contribution to the Christmas fare, now only a week or so away. Back at Jouvancourt, disappointed that our mission had failed, we took off *en route* for our home airfield. It had felt strange to be standing for a few hours on French soil which had so recently been in the hands of the Luftwaffe.

One evening after dinner in the Mess I passed Rory's living quarters and heard music. I stopped and listened and was soon invited to join Rory who already had an audience sitting on the floor as Beethoven's Emperor Concerto filled the room.

Earlier in the year 1944 we had acquired a new type of American-made AI equipment called 'Ash'. It was light-weight and the whole of the electronics, including transmitter receiver and antenna system were contained in a water-tight capsule looking like a 500 lb bomb. It worked in the ultra high frequency microwave band of 5 cm ('X band' to be precise). It had a good, high resolution picture which was perhaps better in performance than the SCR 720. We made plans for fitting it on Mosquitoes.

Soon 1945 was upon us. It was now clear that the Germans would be defeated. We were bombing Berlin heavily. Likewise, our American friends also bombed on numerous daytime raids. The Russians were closing in ready to attack the city. Enemy activity was slackening. We too were almost static — Nazi Germany was paralysed. The general feeling within 100 Group is very difficult to describe. It was a strange stage in an organization that had played a part in an enormous arena, whose orchestra had gone on strike. All I could do was to keep in touch with our external contacts. I felt we should not be feeble.

On 22nd April 1945 news filtered through that Hitler was making his last stand in Berlin. He was a finished man and committed suicide in his bunker on 29th April. At General Eisenhower's headquarters the unconditional terms of surrender were signed at midnight, 8th May 1945.*

* Churchill, *The Second World War* Vol. VI page 433.

Cartoon by the author shows daily inspection by radar maintenance mechanics on a Mosquito. They are busy with the 'black boxes'.

This cartoon by the author depicts a radio countermeasures Flying Fortress, bristling with radio jammer equipment antennas, being loaded with 'window'. Simultaneously the aircraft engines were starting up, thereby causing chaos on the tarmac!

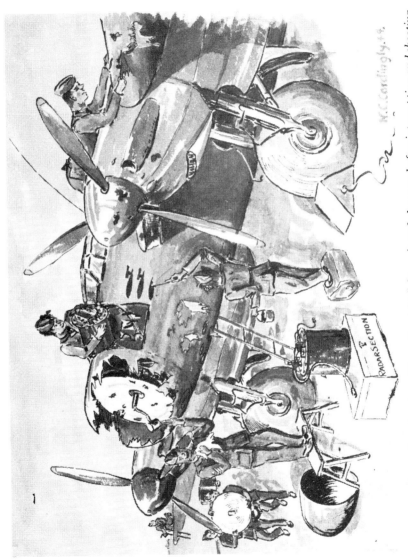

Cartoon by the author showing a Mosquito night fighter aircraft damaged after intercepting and shooting down a 'buzz-bomb'.

Cartoon by the author showing a radio altimeter being calibrated. (The Squadron Commander operated at night, flying at very low level — an 'impossible' feat.)

Chapter 15

1945: AFTERMATH EVENTS

In this phase, after the German surrender, we had a programme of visits to the Continent where the Army was already mopping up and the remnants of the Luftwaffe were awaiting movement instructions. One morning Wing/Cdr. Tait told me he was about to embark on a Mosquito flight to observe areas of Germany over which he had flown on operations. He asked me whether I would like to go with him. I jumped at the idea and we left from one of our adjacent airfields, Swanton Morley. We flew over Brussels, Cologne, Essen, Dortmund and Eindhoven. It did seem strange to be speeding along in a Mosquito at low level without enemy interference. Krupps Works at Essen was a terrible sight, devastation everywhere with masses of twisted metal on a bed of rubble. We flew over the dams where Dr Barnes Wallis's special bouncing bombs dropped by Bomber Command had been effective. Lastly we went to Hamburg. The city was not recognizable with a vast area in ruins. This was a sorry sight I shall not forget. It was 15th April and as we landed at Swanton Morley with spring in the air and everything green and pleasant we were overcome by its contrast with the scenes of devastation we had just witnessed.

The Group was anxious to see enemy radar ground stations and to examine the German aircraft. We flew to Denmark and landed at Grove airfield where we saw lines of abandoned Luftwaffe aircraft with propellers removed. Our team was based at Schleswig-Holstein and had come to witness the interrogation of the Luftflotte-Reich HQ. staff who were housed in a wooded camp site.

Our interrogation took place at the Stadt Hamburg Hotel at Schleswig-Holstein. Air Commodore Rory Chisholm, together with an official army interrogator were present to direct proceedings. The first man we met was General Martinez: his rank being similar to our own Director General of Signals. Some German officers belonging to a technical branch were rather difficult and were not very forthcoming. I remember seeing a German naval officer. He was very arrogant and this was a definite black mark against him. We also met a civilian

100 Group visit to Luftflotte-Reich HQ in woods at Schleswig-Holstein. Air Vice-Marshal Addison (AOC) standing to the right of the signpost, with Wing/Cdr. Tait on extreme right. To left of signpost are Group Captain Tester and Sqn/Ldr. Bailee. Photograph taken during visit to Schleswig-Holstein.

A German officer enters the Stadt-Hamburg Hotel where the RAF interrogation of the Luftflotte-Reich personnel started in earnest. (Crown copyright photograph)

Dr Cockburn (on right) TRE scientist, interrogates personnel in Luftflotte-Reich HQ. (Crown copyright photograph)

A German technician holds up a piece of their radar equipment at the Luftflotte-Reich HQ in the woods at Schleswig-Holstein. (Crown copyright photograph)

Junkers 88 fighter with SN2 radar antennas. (Crown copyright photograph)

Junkers 88 fitted with special plywood nosepiece to take 9.1 cm radar scanner (experimental) called 'Berlin Gerate'. (Crown copyright photograph)

Junkers 88 aircraft with pointed nose fitted with aerials for Fuge 218. Wing/Cdr. J.B. Tait stands in foreground. (Crown copyright photograph)

technologist who belonged to the Telefunken set-up. Altogether we got some interesting intelligence including details of night fighter equipment. They were also working on a new interceptor device using a lead-sulphide cell for the detection of heat from aircraft engine exhausts. We made plans to visit other important German radar ground installations such as Kleine Strauber (Little Screw) and the Wurtzburg radar stations. These were both the German equivalent of our GCI stations. They had a parabolic reflector which rotated on a turntable. After the interrogation our next plan was to visit a large fixed radar station which we heard was sited on the Danish island of Romo. I flew to Eggebeck with Wing/Cdr. Tait in a German Storch which he had managed to commandeer. We took off and eventually sighted the little island. Wing/Cdr. Tait said he would land on the large sandy beach and we orbited the area — it looked all right for landing. Suddenly we saw below us, perhaps 100 feet, a horse and cart being driven by a man who pointed feverishly inland. We deduced we were unsafe to land on the shoreside. We therefore landed on a nice flat surface near by and were soon joined by the man with the horse and cart. He spoke good English and told us he was the Mayor of Romo. He said he wanted to warn us about the minefield which was in the undergrowth along the shore. He told us it was unsafe to walk about and suggested we stay in the plane for ten minutes and then take off. Meanwhile he would go back to the centre of the island and put a marker on a safe field to enable us to land. At the appointed time 'Tirpitz Tait' took off and orbited the area. The marked field proved to be very small indeed but with great skill 'Tirpitz' managed to land safely, though damaging the propeller on a wooden fence post. With the Mayor's help we managed to contact Eggebeck airfield and arranged for a new propeller and a mechanic to be flown out while we remained on the island. The Mayor, acting as our guide, took us to the huge German radar installation. There was an extensive concrete blast-proof underground shelter, a Todt construction. It was used as a store for radio components and a workshop-cum-laboratory which had a solitary German technician still in attendance. The island had its own charm and was a little windswept. There were plenty of wild flowers. We made a thorough examination of the huge stacked aerial array which looked out towards the sea in a north-easterly direction. The local children and inhabitants rallied round to watch and our new propeller was fixed before long. Just before take-off, we found, tucked inside the cockpit on a seat, a number of boxes containing fresh eggs. A little note was also put in saying 'A little greet from the people of Romo'.

Photograph showing 'Tirpitz Tait' and the author ready to set off for the Island of Romo in a German Storch.

Photograph showing the Mayor of Romo with his wife. The Mayor had earlier warned us of the danger of minefields.

The Storch's propeller was damaged while landing on the improvised airfield at Romo. This photograph shows local children who gathered round while the propeller was replaced.

A giant German radar ground station (Mammout) photographed by the author in Romo. (Crown copyright photograph)

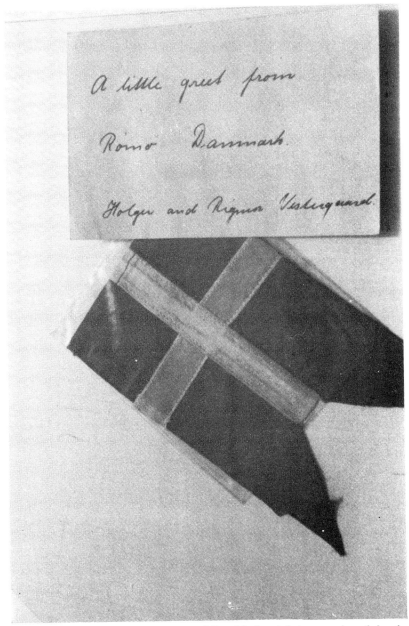

Photograph showing the message and Danish flag left in our aircraft by the islanders of Romo before we took off.

Also enclosed were some small Danish flags. We took off safely and both felt happy, realizing the Danes had come out of the German occupation fairly unscathed.

I had yet another flight to Schleswig-Holstein as the AOC was anxious to see for himself the Luftwaffe's fighter aircraft and other aspects of the German set-up. We went out in an Oxford twin-engined aircraft with Wing/Cdr. Tait acting as our pilot. The airfield at Copenhagen was littered with abandoned fighter aeroplanes. On our flight I happened to tell the AOC that my wife had a fairly elderly aunt in Copenhagen and that during the war we had had very little news of her. She, like her classicist brother, was a good linguist and knew most of the Danish professional people. The AOC agreed that we would have some time to spare and we went to have lunch at a well-known hotel. We were welcomed by the manager and had a good meal. I explained my difficulty in getting news of my wife's aunt and the manager quickly got hold of a person who knew the lady. They promised to try to get a message to her and we said we would be having tea at the Tivoli tea-shop and would keep a look out for her. It so happened that the tea-shop was serving strawberry cream teas and we all (an Air Vice-Marshal, two Wing Commanders and a Squadron Leader of the RAF) sat round a table and started to enjoy the strawberries. Into the centre of the room appeared a lady formally dressed in a black costume and black straw hat and carrying a rolled umbrella. She came up to me and, obviously not recognizing me after a gap of several years since my wedding, said, "Excuse me, I'm trying to find an RAF officer, Wing Commander Cordingly." Of course, she was amazed to find she had picked on me and we all enjoyed tea while talking about the way the Gestapo had treated her and some of her friends. Before leaving to join our motor transport we called her a cab which, incidentally, was operated from a charcoal burning device at the rear of the vehicle! We all emptied our pockets and were busy filling her handbag with sweets and chocolate and cigarettes when we became aware of a curious crowd collecting to observe our generosity. These onlookers were duly sent off by a wave of the black umbrella!

My several visits to Schleswig-Holstein meeting the defeated enemy personnel of the Luftflotte-Reich Heaquarters, also seeing abandoned aircraft and radar ground stations, had a profound effect on me. Therefore I feel I must express my personal comments on the situation as I saw it. The RAF HQ 100 Group with its technical superiority and sophisticated equipment certainly had the edge on the Luftwaffe. I

In the Tivoli tea-shop, Copenhagen — my wife's elderly aunt, Miss Louisa Dale, who was a resident linguist. She 'surfaced' there after our attempt to locate her, when my AOC and I visited the city after the war.

could imagine the frustration caused to them by the RAF's counter-measures, radar and homing devices. It seemed to me that the German night fighter operation system was practically paralysed. Seeing a number of German aircraft fitted with various aerial systems in the form of what appeared to be improvised dipoles attached to the nose and fuselage it was evident that their technical boffins had problems. We saw a number of Junkers 88s each with a different system in addition to their formidable SN2 airborne radar. One aircraft had an experimental plywood nose designed to take a centimetric parabolic antenna belonging to their new Berlin Gerate AI. Another aircraft was bristling with all manner of aerial systems, mostly dipoles of unknown wavelength with improvised fittings. It was obvious they had been making a great effort to keep abreast of developments so essential for night operations.

With great rejoicing all over the country VE day came and passed. Back at Group Headquarters I got on with my task at the office, my mind still full of our fleeting visits to meet the vanquished. My job was to record the salient points of our visits to the German installations. All I wanted in future was a peaceful existence; but it was not to be. Air Ministry wrote to me. I was to be posted to work in the next phase of the war against Japan, using my experience in radar interception coupled with radio countermeasures. I was to join the staff of 'Tiger Force', whose Commander-in-Chief was Air Marshal Sir Hugh Pugh Lloyd. The new force was at that time being formed at a headquarters in Bushey Park near Teddington. My family, who had been living in Scotland, were home again in Golders Green, with my wife's parents, who had been evacuated to Marlborough College during the war period. I used to motor every day to our Bushey headquarters. The HQ staff, like me, was undergoing special training relating to intelligence information about Japanese life and a jungle warfare survival course. I had to understand the many aspects of their communications and work. The general plan for the future of the force had been outlined to us all. I, for example, was to go to Okinawa. We were to be flown out in Britain's new Lincoln bombers. Many things were somewhat vague though we had some directives from the Air Ministry too.

One morning some time after my arrival at Bushey we were all summoned to hear a message from Sir Hugh, our C.-in-C. He looked a bit grim and serious and told us that all our training efforts with the Tiger Force were in vain because of the important news he had just had. On the night of 6th August the Americans had dropped an atomic bomb on Nagasaki and Hiroshima. This action, of course, paralysed Japan. The news sounded pretty grim. The C.-in-C.'s initial serious look changed to one of smiles as he told us we could all stay put and wait for further orders.

Yet another chapter of my career with the RAF came to an end here: I now had to wait a period to see what the Air Ministry wished to do with my services. I soon received a message that I should report to the Officer in Charge of Signals Plans at the Air Ministry Directorate. I did this and was told that I would be posted to HQ RAF Mediterranean/Middle East (Med/ME) Cairo. My new chief was to be Air Vice-Marshal Aitken, the Chief Signals Officer. I heard that my tour of duty would be six months: in other words I should expect to be demobilized on or about March 1946. Before starting my new duties it was arranged that I should accompany Air Commodore Weston, of the Directorate of Signals, on a brief visit to the area. The Air Commodore was quite an interesting and very pleasant character. He was very tall, so much so that his Air Ministry nickname was 'Lofty Weston'. I felt dwarfed when I stood by him. On the 24th September the Air Commodore and I flew from Blackheath in a Dakota with an SAAF aircrew. Our destination was Athens where we landed at Hassani airfield. We called on the Signals staff of the Royal Hellenic Air Force. I remember meeting a Greek wing commander who had the fascinating name of Dimitri Theodossiades. I later met him again and learned that he was ADC to King Peter. We had a number of other signals matters to attend to and, our business finished, we flew on to Cairo where we landed at Almaza Airport. At HQ Med/ME which was to be my home, we called on the CSO Air Vice-Marshal Aitken, my new chief. He was indeed very surprised to learn that we had known each other at the outbreak of the war when I was still a civilian! (I have already mentioned our meeting when he and I shared lock-up garages in Stanmore.) Strange! — It is a small world! Air Commodore Weston and I stayed for three days which gave us the opportunity of getting to know people at the headquarters. I found most of the serving officers very helpful and was happy to find I would be working with an old Air Ministry Directorate of Radar colleague Wing/Cdr. Gilbart-Smith. I was able to fix my living quarters and arrangements were made for me to live at a small Hotel-cum-Pensione for the duration of my tour while attached to HQ Med/ME.

On the 27th September we left Cairo and flew over the Libyan Plateau to El Adem where we spent some time on signals matters. The next day we flew on to Luqa airfield in Malta to see the Station Signals Officer and his set-up. I visited the workshop where one of my radar officers, Flt./Lt. Willis, had done a first-class job coping with the AI equipped Beaufighters ever since he was sent out by me when I was at the Air Ministry. At that time there was enormous pressure to defend Malta. Later, on 28th September, we left Malta and flew to Marseilles Istres airfield, refuelled, and then flew to the UK landing at Hurn. I was now to have a week's leave prior to making my return visit to Cairo. I made the best of this precious week at home with the family. My little daughters Juliet and Rosemary were growing fast and we all had a feeling of joy. Black-out restrictions were no more and the original bomb damage had been put right. I tried to persuade my wife to take up painting again and she actually embarked on an oil portrait of me in uniform. Having spent most of the wartime days looking after our daughters she was glad to have an opportunity to take up palette and brushes once again.

It suddenly occurred to me that I ought to visit my old firm to see how it had coped in the war period. Nearly five years had passed since I reported to Whitehall to start my service life in the RAF. I telephoned the firm and drove off to North Finchley where I met Russell Wright, my old managing director. I had a wonderful reception and met old colleagues and the remaining directors, E.E. Burnside and Harold Quinton who was looking after the engineering side of the business. Dennis Wright, son of Tom Wright, was then looking after works production. One of my engineers, an interesting character called Arthur Long had been supervising the X-ray tube and rectifying valve development and production work. He was a capable man and an expert glass technologist. He knew all the tricks for making metal-to-glass seals. Before leaving I had a long chat with Russell Wright who assured me he would be happy if I could see my way clear to join the company and continue my old work. I thanked him and said I was still heavily committed with the RAF.

Chapter 16

POSTING TO HQ Med/ME (CAIRO)

I had already packed and was ready for my Middle East trip. I left the UK by air on the 16th October 1945, flying in a Dakota *en route* for Cairo. We stopped at Luqa in Malta. The aircraft was carrying a number of civilians including members of the Royal Shakespeare Company in ENSA uniforms. John Gielgud was one of our important passengers. We crossed the Mediterranean and headed for the North Coast of Africa where we stoped at El Adem, a hutted transit camp site in the desert. There was just enough sleeping accommodation and I was given a small room adjacent to the one allocated to John Gielgud. We were all up at dawn and the plane took off in the morning sunlight. There was a spectacular sight as we were crossing the Nile Delta which was veiled with early morning mist, pearlish-violet in colour. In Cairo's built up area the tall minarets and domes of mosques pierced the mist, their tips gleaming brightly in the sunlight. Our plane approached Cairo and after orbiting we descended through the mist and touched down at Almaza Airport. The morning air was like champagne as we made our way to the terminal building after the fascinating and breath-taking signs of sunrise over the veiled capital. I stopped a taxi and was driven straight to HQ RAF Med/ME. The headquarters building was quite an imposing structure. At the base was a flight of steps up one side and another at the far side. I left my luggage and went up to the floor which housed the signals branch. I reported to Air Vice-Marshal Aitken, the CSO. He welcomed me like a long lost brother and I met most of the officers in the branch, including an old Air Ministry friend Wing/Cdr. Gilbart-Smith. Strangely enough I was to meet him again at Caserta in Italy later on.

Cairo was an entirely different environment compared with most habitats I had experienced with the RAF. For one thing the air was fresh and a little dry; it was comfortably warm. Physically I felt fit and healthy and all set for a job of work. Of course, Cairo had distinctive smells and noises — donkeys and camels and motor taxis all contributed to the sounds in the street. There were also horse-drawn gharries. In the back streets there was a hubbub of high-pitched jabbering in Arab tongues. The pavements were often littered with discarded bits of chewed sugar-cane and it was all very unhygienic!

The CSO told me next morning that he was planning to make a number of visits to RAF units in Palestine and also to units in the coastal areas of North Africa, east of the Nile Delta. This latter flight of approximately 2,800 miles would take at least a week and might entail paying calls to other signals units in the Mediterranean. He explained that I would accompany him in a twin-engined Expediter which he would fly personally. We would have to stop a day or so and spend the night at certain places. He mentioned Benghazi, Castel Benito and Algiers. We would in all probability visit station signals officers in Luqa (Malta) and Elmas (Sardinia). Also there was quite a lot of work to be done in Naples and he thought we might fly on there from Sardinia. I thought these flight plans would keep us very busy and wondered what sort of personalities we would be meeting. There was a total of sixteen units we hoped to call upon! We planned to start the trip on 7th November 1945, with a short visit to the signals set-up at Quastina in Palestine the day before. On our return that evening we went up to the roof top of the headquarters. It had a roof garden with a bar. It was very pleasant after work to sit in the cool evening air and have a chat, while above in the sky the kites were busy doing their aerobatics and gliding in the thermals. Although there was a cool breeze there was quite a lot of stored heat radiated from the roof surface. Traffic noise was easily heard amidst the chattering of the birds in the adjacent palm trees. I went back to my hotel for dinner and found an army major cracking a joke with a young-looking captain in the dining-room. As usual we were served with roast water buffalo and sweet potatoes, with local fresh dates and bananas to follow. We got talking and the major introduced himself as Paul Slatter, an ex-bank manager. (Later on, after my time in Cairo, I met Paul again by chance at Heathrow Airport with his wife and discovered that they were embarking on the same holiday cruise as Mollie and me. We all became firm friends.) I went into the lounge afterwards for a cup of Turkish coffee: sweet, sticky syrup but good flavour. With thoughts about the trip next day I retired to bed.

I was up at an early hour and went off to the Heliopolis Palace Hotel for breakfast. The hotel was a kind of transit camp. The building was adjacent to the airfield and it was convenient for short stops. The architecture was unusual, it resembled a cathedral. It had its own sparrow inmates, thus when eating bacon and eggs and toast the birds were quick to fly down to snatch a few crumbs and titbits. I met the AVM and very soon we loaded the Expediter with our luggage. The ground crew had completed their checks and forms were signed. Air Vice-Marshal Aitken looked very smart and had the air of a civilian airline pilot. We settled in to the cockpit and made ready. We started the two engines and gave them full revs. The chocks were removed from under the wheels and we taxied off. It was a superb morning and the air was warming up in the sunshine. We flew over the Delta area and then over the Libyan Plateau. Our first call was Matruh where we contacted our station signals officer. Off again, we followed the coastline to El Adem for a brief inspection, then straight on to Benina in Benghazi where we stopped for a time. I should add here that such a flight made a deep impression on me. We were, of course, covering the tracks taken by Rommel and Montgomery during the El Alamein desert campaign and were able to see old wrecked tanks and field guns partially covered with sand. Even the harbour of Tripoli was littered with wrecked ships, some lying on their sides. All around the battle scene could be imagined. On numerous occasions during our flight over the coastal region I would see a bedraggled line of Arabs following what appeared to be natural tracks. The men were in groups following the women and a few goats and sometimes a donkey.

We stopped for one night at Benghazi and pressed on next day calling at Marble Arch and Castel Beneto. There was an odd form of transit camp in this region manned by RAF with a senior officer in charge. Close by a number of Arabs with their families and animals were camped. We fed well and enjoyed the beer provided. The next morning we left this station and set course across the coast and flew to Luqa in Malta. This was my second visit. We spent some time with the station signals officer then arranged transport and called on the RAF personnel. We lunched at the Turf Club which was frequented by British service people in Valetta.

We had one night in Malta and next day returned to El Amina, Tunis. Our next port of call was at Maison Blanc in Algiers. This busy place was a full and thriving town. There were a number of French aeroplanes parked on the airfield. We contacted our signals officer and then spent one night there. The next day, feeling refreshed, we flew to Oran, La Senia and Bleda. We had been away for nearly a week and the CSO decided to leave Bleda and to fly across the coast to Sardinia where we landed at Elmas. This fascinating little island had a peculiar charm: a little bit of Italy. We left Elmas and flew direct to Naples where we stayed at the RAF Mess located in the old Palace building at HQ Caserta. We had discussion with service personnel relating to my signals plans mission. The general situation in Italy was favourable and there were signs of recovery from war restrictions. The next day the CSO decided to return to Cairo. I had to stay on a few days to complete my planned programme.

I decided to stay at Caserta where the RAF people were living under canvas. I therefore moved into the tent allocated to me and arranged my luggage. I unpacked a clean shirt and left it hanging on a coat hanger which I placed on a hook at the top of the tent pole. There was an Officers' Mess in an adjacent building so after a refreshing drink there I returned to my tent and changed into my clean shirt before going over to have dinner. The weather was clear and very warm and that evening turned out to be rather hilarious. I took a seat at a table in the dining-room and was just enjoying the soup course when I got a peculiar feeling on my chest. It was a prickly feeling which seemed to move upwards towards my collar. I said to the fellow who was sitting near me, "Excuse me, I must undo my top shirt button to relieve this prickly heat feeling." When I got to the button near the top my fingers encountered a strange wriggling movement and suddenly a medium-sized lizard jumped out and fell into my soup plate! Well, this was no joke for me, but between laughter by all present I abandoned my soup plate and prepared to start the meal all over again. We all agreed that while my shirt was hanging on the tent pole the lizard probably crept in to snooze while the midday sun warmed the canvas outside.

One of the guests staying with us at Caserta was the well-known scientist Alexander Fleming, discoverer of penicillin. He was lecturing on antibiotics, I believe. I met a signals officer staying in the Mess and during the course of conversation I found myself being invited to meet a local scientist in Naples. He was Professor Dohrn, Director of the Naples Marine Biological Station. He was an authority on octopus behaviour and had a special aquarium devoted to these creatures. He invited me to look around the station and there I also met his son. They were Germans and were very interesting people to meet. I was amazed that the Professor could do a number of tests to demonstrate the psychological behaviour of the octopus. He used some coloured discs which, when dropped into the water, stimulated certain reactions associated with eating habits. It was a fascinating demonstration. Before leaving Naples I enjoyed a very pleasant evening with them on another occasion, meeting Mrs Dohrn, and we talked the whole evening about the marine biological work that was being undertaken.

On 16th November 1945 I joined a SAAF Dakota for my flight back to Cairo. I reckoned I had been absent from HQ Med/ME for a little over a fortnight. It was amazing how much could be packed into a short time. A personal visit and verbal exchanges face to face seemed to be far more efficacious than a lot of paper work and communication by wire or radio.

Now safely back in Cairo I was able to get to grips with other duties. I had, for example, to call at the British Embassy to sign the visitors' book and to leave my card. I had a dinner engagement at the Embassy's Oriental Secretary's house. The hostess was Audrey Ravensdale, a charming lady. She also invited two of Cairo's influential Copts — Edward and Marie Wissa. I found them very pleasant and from that evening onwards we became good friends.

Since my tour with the CSO I had had some considerable correspondence to get through. In late November I had further demands on my services which obviously called for a fairly brief visit. Caserta was my first priority where I stayed in the HQ at the Royal Palace and was met by my old colleague Wing/Cdr. Norman Gilbart-Smith. I had barely been at Caserta for a few minutes when I had to deal with some signals emanating from HQ Med/ME.

Living conditions in the palace were pretty crude: I found the so-called 'toilet' very off-putting — no flushing WC system, only a little round hole in the middle of a cold stone floor — enough said! The building otherwise was comfortable. I slept reasonably well and was up at 6.30 a.m. and found Gilbart-Smith. He and I, together with another wing commander, were able to go riding on some fine Arab horses which were left by the Germans when they evacuated the town. The three of us rode up the steep hill and then through a cultivated area full of ripening peaches. The ride back to the palace developed into a fastish canter and we felt full of fresh morning air as we went in for an excellent breakfast.

I had other visits to make — to Udine and to the Royal Hellenic Air Force. I decided it would be as well to fly back to Cairo first and this I did.

When I was ready to carry out my proposed visit to Udine I flew with a colleague via Rome to Treviso where we picked up motor transport. We were fortunate enough to be able to stay in Venice for a short while. The Luna Hotel was a first-rate place to stay and was patronized by RAF personnel in transit. The weather was seasonal for late November. We had a very short gondola trip but it was too cold to go far: we gave up at the Rialto Bridge. St Mark's Square made the usual colourful scene picked out by shafts of sunlight amidst the colony of pigeons. A wing commander from HQ Med/ME joined me and we boarded a water bus. At Treviso we went in search of our transport for the journey to Udine which was somewhat less than 100 miles. The RAF was already established at Udine and on arrival we checked ourselves in. The Officers' Mess, which had been used in grand style by the Luftwaffe during the war period, was an elegant building of good architecture. We heard that it had been occupied by the Russians who were reluctant to leave when the British Army moved in. They were not entirely friendly to us, we gathered, and when eventually they evacuated the building they machine-gunned the fresh water storage tanks so during our visit we had to drink borrowed water. In the Mess that evening we sampled some of the local wines and it was simply pouring with rain as we bade farewell to our chaps in charge and set off for Treviso. We had a fairly dicey journey back in the motor transport. It began to get dark and the road, as left by retreating armies, was far from safe. We often had to negotiate a Bailey bridge and sometimes had to push the vehicle through the mud. By a minor miracle we reached Treviso and eventually flew back to Naples via Rome.

My last call on this rather restricted visit was to have a final meeting with the Royal Hellenic Air Force signals personnel. To save time in the long run it was convenient to return to Cairo and next day I was back in Hassani, Athens after a longish delay.

I stayed at headquarters and joined Wing Commander Dimitri Theodossiades for dinner at the Mess and for drinks afterwards. Here we mainly drank the local brew 'Retsina', made from pine cones. The acquired taste was a little like diluted disinfectant! I was persuaded to sample the ouzo — this drink in my opinion is a little rough and not to be made a habit of! During the evening I happened to comment on the beauty of the night with its full moon and said I had heard that to stand in the Parthenon in the moonlight was something one ought to do once in a lifetime. Dimitri agreed and said he would arrange for me to go there. He said he would drive up to the Acropolis and borrow the key from the custodian. As he was an ADC to King Peter of Greece he knew most of the important people. As we reached the top of the Acropolis the sight of the Parthenon in the balmy evening air was a thing to behold. Theo returned with the keys and as we walked up to the entrance I was fascinated by the smooth curved channels that had been cut by wheeled vehicles such as chariots into the marble pavement. The smooth channels caught the gleaming moonlight and one was able to make out a pattern of contrasting shadows. We walked through and up to the steps of the Parthenon. Here I became entranced by the moonlit curvature of the marble pillars and the beams supporting the main structures. We stood and talked while gazing at that wonderful spectacle. Shadows of the pillars were cast across the smooth marble paving stones burnished by many feet through the ages. With the memory of these breath-taking sights and special thanks to Theo for making them possible, I returned to my hotel. The next morning I arrived back in Cairo HQ.

Time was flying rapidly and the Christmas season was nearly upon us. I had a telephone call one day from my wife's cousin, Willie Houston. He was a very important man in BOAC. In past years he had served with the RAF and later on, based at Croydon, became one of Imperial Airways' airline pilots blazing the trail — or, should I say, exploring new airline routes which are now in general use. At this time he was living in Heliopolis. Before Christmas he made a short visit to the UK and happened to call at our home in Golders Green while the family were recording Christmas messages to be flown to me as a Christmas present. Willie was able to take the recording back with him and then he rang me to ask if I would like to visit him and collect it. I did not bother to take a taxi and instead I travelled by Cairo's electric tramway. It was noisy but efficient — that journey to Heliopolis was quite something! I walked the last few yards to the two-storey house where Willie lived with his wife and son. After a pleasant visit I returned to my hotel bearing the whole family's messages recorded on a gramophone record. It was a great undertaking and it was wonderful for me to hear the voices of my wife and daughters.

It was customary within the RAF serving in the Middle East for the officers to help serve Christmas dinner to the other ranks. On Christmas Day I joined other officers and went to Kasra Nil Barracks. The cooks were busy putting the finishing touches to the sweets and puddings. The airmen fed at tables in the open air and we all had a joke to share as we officers, acting as waiters, served lashings of beer. The cooks piled up plates with turkey, sausages and vegetables. In the trees and bushes near the cookhouse the chattering of sparrows and sounds of the local doves could be heard, whilst in nearby bushes the hoopoes were busy probing for insects with their pickaxe beaks. We continued to do our stint and all shared the enjoyment and the beer with the airmen. Altogether it was a thoroughly jolly occasion. Once plates and cutlery were cleared and everything was tidied up I returned to the hotel where the Christmas spirit was well under way. Everyone was busy putting up decorations and adorning an artificial Christmas tree. We were to have our dinner later in the evening.

Our Christmas dinner party was soon in full swing. Our soffragi (servants), dressed in white galabiyas with tarbooshes on their heads, did us proud while cracking little jokes in friendly fun. We drank local canned beer which was quite palatable. The empty cans were lightweight and made of aluminium. I am ashamed to say that someone started to toss empty beer cans out of the windows, which the kites, wheeling airborne in the half-light, occasionally tried to intercept! The Arab waiters did us well and occasionally joined in the parlour games. The evening passed all too quickly and I was glad to retire to my bedroom. It had been my third Christmas spent away from home and family.

The New Year 1946 was to be an eventful time for me. Most of my work in the weeks that had passed had been fruitful and I felt I still had a lot to learn particularly in areas unknown to me such as the Persian Gulf and the region covering the oil pipeline. I also had a commitment to visit Luxor which would be tackled when a suitable occasion arrived.

Later, whilst still at HQ Med/ME I received a message which gave me a thrill. I learned that I had been awarded an OBE in King George VI's New Year's Honours List. Furthermore, according to the *London Gazette*, I had been granted a permanent commission as a regular Wing Commander. All this news was overwhelming and I was kept busy answering letters from friends in the UK all bearing messages of congratulations.

My next immediate job was to complete my Palestine trip. On 5th January I flew by Dakota from Almaza Airport straight to Lydda Airport. Motor transport collected me and we drove to Jerusalem where I stayed at the Officers' Mess which was immediately opposite the Jaffa Gateway. To be staying in the Holy City for a few days naturally stimulated my desire when off duty to learn all about the area frequented by Christ. An officer in the Mess managed to organize an archaeology student to show me round and to outline the history in this holy place. I met him one evening and we fixed a meeting time for a tour. I found the RAF was resident in part of the King David Hotel. Here we had a well-organized signals and communications set-up. At that time there was much unrest and friction between the Palestine folk. The Haganea, a kind of resistance commando unit, was a force not to be lightly dismissed. They did quite a lot to upset plans and caused trouble in certain areas.

During my stay with one of our signals personnel we motored to

Mount Carmel. Here at the top was a radar station looking seawards. The station was substantially protected with a circular sandbagged wall. I met the people in charge and we discussed signals matters. The view from the top of the mount was really magnificent. There were numerous wild flowers popping up from the grassy slopes. Looking down to the beach there were signs of local fishing activity and it was interesting to behold a few camels gently plodding along the seashore. Several days after my visit to Mount Carmel news came through that the Haganea had climbed to the top of the mount and had left a booby trap in the form of an ordinary haversack with a Jaffa orange sitting snugly on the top — this was hanging on the sandbagged walls. The RAF Sergeant in charge of the radar station, whom I had met so recently, was killed outright by this.

One morning I met the student of history and archaeology at the King David Hotel and we wandered off to the Jaffa Gate. He then said he would like to show me the place where the original Temple keystone was cut from the limestone which forms part of the city's foundation. We walked around the wall to the left of the Jaffa Gate and came to a cavernous hole in the wall and then scrambled inside. My good friend had brought with him an electric torch and with its help he explained the geological formation was all limestone below the city and was called King Solomon's Mine. There was a cavernous arch running in all directions below. Here we discovered a large bat colony hanging from the limestone roof. Close by, my attention was drawn to a long chiselled channel, triangular in shape. This was the place from which the cheese-wedge shaped keystone had been cut for the original Temple which was rent asunder. The casual visitor to Jerusalem would probably never have the chance to see this amazing historical evidence and I felt very privileged. We went back to the Jaffa Gate and entered the city, slowly descending the steps where the milling crowd was busy with displays of goods. The smell from the spice market was overpowering. I stopped to look at an old Arab's wares. He had a tray piled high with shelled nuts. I asked for some walnuts and he said to me, "You my friend?" I said, "Yes, why not?" Then he said, "What about the Jews?" I replied that they were my friends also. "No," he said, "you are not my friend." As I paid for the nuts he drew the back of his hand across his throat in an unpleasant gesture saying, "I would put their heads in a boiling pot!" I hurried up the steps to the Jaffa Gate and back to the Mess.

Before leaving Jerusalem I was anxious to find time to follow the steps of the Holy Family and walk to Bethlehem, a truly impressive undertaking. I managed to arrange my work schedules and set off. I had a great surprise when looking into the Church of the Nativity. Most of the area was in a cavernous room occupied by numerous shrines of different religious denominations. The actual scene of the Nativity was a very small low place with an awkward entrance. Perhaps the most impressive sight I shall never forget was standing on the Mount of Olives and then surveying the honey-buff buildings dotted about. All the detail of the city was a little difficult to discern in the shimmering morning heat-haze. I hoped tranquillity would be restored to the area one day.

Having completed my signals work in Jerusalem I flew back to Cairo in an Egyptian Airline plane. Seeing the Sinai Desert with its monochrome vistas was a sight to behold. Once back at HQ I was able to complete a report on my visit. I had had a glimpse of the mysterious Holy Land and was glad to have had such a stimulus.

Chapter 17

CAIRO PARTY HIGHLIGHTS

One evening I found myself preparing for yet another dinner party to be given by the Embassy's Oriental Secretary's wife, Audrey Ravensdale. They had invited the American Air Attaché, Capt. Jack Nuttall from the American legation. Jack was an interesting character and had, I imagine, quite an important job in Cairo. We used to meet on occasions at the Shepherds Hotel which was quite a good place for a beer and a chat. On one occasion Jack asked me to book a date in my diary. He was to have a birthday party in his apartment which was situated only a short walk from the Gezira Sporting Club. He said he had invited King Farouk to his party and that he had already accepted.

On the evening of the party I arrived at the ground floor entrance and was waiting for the lift to take me up to the first floor. I noticed a car drive up and a lady stepped out and came towards the lift in the foyer. I explained that I had pressed the 'up' button so she waited. She had a slightly dusky complexion and was dressed in the most expensive attire — an evening dress of a flimsy tulle-like material suitable for a warm evening in Cairo. She was certainly beautifully dressed and I was aware of an exotic perfume which drifted towards my nostrils. The lift arrived and I helped the lady into it. We emerged on the first floor and were received by Jack Nuttall. He introduced us and the lady turned out to be Princess Abbas Halim. She made a few remarks in good English. The Princess was distantly related to King Farouk and her husband was Prince Abbas Halim who apparently did not 'hit it off' with the British during wartime.

Jack had a well-furnished apartment. There was a bar at the end with high stools. We moved over there and I noticed my Copt friend Edward Wissa and his wife Marie. She was dressed smartly for the occasion and sported a special hairstyle. They were most friendly and went out of their way to give me some general hints on the protocol at such an occasion. Already the room was filling up with numerous American officers and their wives. There was much chatter and it was hard to hear and be heard with such a background noise. At last the great moment arrived when Jack announced the arrival of the King. On entering he was received by Jack and led to the centre of the room where he was offered an armchair upholstered in fabric. The King had with him a uniformed Egyptian officer, probably some kind of ADC, and he took a back seat. We all met the King — he had a lively personality, was podgy in appearance and was obviously very much overweight. He was a character I shall never forget. Once seated on the armchair he gathered around him at least four of the pretty American wives in the room. Incidentally this chair was so placed that the cold buffet table was within his reach. I could not help being amused by his tactics — he had one lady on each knee and another two sat on the arms of the chair. His own arms were embracing the females. He started joking and fooling about and amidst the uproar the chair and the King rocked incessantly. Eventually, the chair collapsed with a splitting crack, spilling the great bulk of the playboy King and sending the four ladies rolling on to the floor. There was a great hush and occasional giggles as order was restored and a substitute chair was placed in the middle of the room. By now the other guests were getting hungry because protocol ordained that they must not eat before the King had been served. It was decided that a young wife should offer to fetch the King some food. He accepted the offer and soon the buffet was well patronized. I was feeling hungry too and moved towards the food. I noticed the King was cutting some cold chicken and as he did so the fork fell off his plate on to the floor. I dashed to the buffet table, picked up a clean fork and handed it to the King who accepted it graciously. After the meal was over the King came over to me and said, "The fork — very touching old boy!"

There was an interval for dancing after the meal. I heard the Princess suddenly let out a cry. I hurried towards her and noticed she had a huge insect caught in a fold of the flimsy material of her skirt. I offered to try to extricate the offending creature and she nodded. I gathered the gauzy fabric and found the insect was a huge locust whose barbed legs had got well and truly entangled in the material. After a masterly bit of dexterity I managed to disentangle the barbs, then took it out of the room and released it over the balcony. After this incident I was able to dance with the Princess with a clear conscience.

Later in the evening the King made an announcement, saying he had organized a birthday surprise for Jack Nuttall. The apartment door bell rang and the King himself went to open it. He let in one of his belly dancers and a couple of musicians. King Farouk sat cross-legged on the floor and started to tap a rhythm on a drum made of skin stretched over a pottery pot. He was accompanied by the musicians, one playing a one-string fiddle and the other with a flute-like instrument. The dancer gyrated around the room, belly wobbling, and her contortions were in harmony with the weird music. After the party had been going quite a while I walked out on to the balcony. The evening was mild and a breeze enlivened me. Around midnight it was time for the Princess to leave. When I said goodbye she thanked me for my gallant act of rescue and told me in a low voice that her birthday party was in the near future and she hoped I would come. I thanked her and bade her good-night. I stayed on at the party by Jack's request and then had to wait until King Farouk made his departure. It was well past 2 a.m. when eventually I got back to my hotel.

During my stay in Cairo I was also fortunate enough to meet a person who was steeped in ornithology. He was a Mr Greaves and lived in the Zamalek suburb of Cairo. I found him a fascinating character whose main interest in birds was their migration habits. During a break from my work at HQ I was able to visit him and his wife for tea one afternoon. I had many questions to put to him because I had seen a 'V' formation of birds in flight over Cairo. He said they might have been storks. I had a great interest in the egrets whose habit at sunset was to flock in to roost in banyan trees on the Nile bank. We met one evening to observe this phenomenon. It coincided with his work on the migration of pied wagtails. Every night they flocked to roost on the Nile bridge ledges and sometimes on the muddy verges of the River Nile. Mr Greaves had a migration problem and wanted to mark all wagtails before they set off on their flight. He had conceived the idea of marking their plumage with a special quick-drying and safe magenta-coloured dye. He had already received samples from ICI. His plan was first to observe the bush on the Nile bank where the birds packed together to roost. We spent an evening after sunset and noticed a particular bush which was full of wagtails sitting side by side. All was quiet and it was almost dark. A day or so later we decided to carry out the marking plan. We waited until it was practically dark and there were few people about and then he carried a bucket of water to the site together with a stirrup pump and mixer. He poured the dye from a bottle into the bucket and gave it all a good stir. I then took over and placed the stirrup pump into the bucket and started to pump up and down. Meanwhile he directed the fine spray emitted from the nozzle at the end of the flexible pipe through the branches and leaves all over the bush. The birds did not make a noise and when we had exhausted the whole contents of the bucket we packed up and went back, agreeing to meet at sunset next evening. Sure enough the wagtails, now a pretty pink, came in next evening to roost on the bridge ledges and in the bush. We were satisfied with our nocturnal experiment and hoped it would contribute to a little scientific knowledge about the migration habits of pied wagtails. Unfortunately I never heard anything further from Mr Greaves because when I eventually left Cairo we lost touch.

In due time the birthday party of Princess Abbas Halim drew near. As I was not sure how to reply to the invitation I telephoned my Copt friends. Marie told me that the usual procedure was to send some flowers with a visiting card on the day of the birthday. I therefore went to the florist and arranged for flowers to be delivered to her palace which was a simple and quite ordinary building set back in Cairo's Garden City. On the evening of the party there were quite a number of guests queueing up to be received. It so happened that I found myself standing behind the British Ambassador, Lord Killearn. I was tickled pink with his diplomatic behaviour. He was clutching a small bunch of lovely violets in his hand behind his back. It was nevertheless an appropriate gesture, I thought, as he bowed and handed the Princess the flowers. She welcomed me with a smile and afterwards I wandered off to look for my Copt friends. The evening passed fairly rapidly with an abundance of drinks and plenty of food on the mountainous buffet. There were intervals for dancing and at some point I happened to say to Edward and Marie, "What happens next?" They explained that at the actual hour of the Princess's birth we would all line up facing the Prince who would be standing on a dais. The Prince would pour out a drink of his own choice and hand it to each person as he approached. The glass must then be raised to the health of the Princess and the drink consumed in one gulp. When my turn came I approached the Prince who took a tumbler and proceeded to pour out a very large whisky. For some reason my measure looked a lot larger than others being dispensed by the Prince. My heart sank, realizing that I had already had several drinks during the evening before hearing about this ceremony. I thought, 'How on earth can I drink this in one?' Not wishing to give offence I raised the tumbler and knocked back the potent liquor and then returned to the party. I happened to see the Wissas and said, "I have had too much to drink, what shall I do?" They told me I could not leave yet and sat me down to rest; the evening continued. Eventually it was announced that breakfast would shortly be served. This seemed a good idea and I had a small portion but soon began to feel ill. The Wissas told me I could not leave until the Princess had retired from the party. Eventually the moment came and thus the sun was up and shining as I left the palace and walked slowly quite a long way back to my hotel. I do not know how I managed it! On reaching my bedroom I passed out on the bed and slept for twelve hours.

Some time later Edward Wissa invited me to call and see him and Marie at their Garden City home in Cairo. I went one evening and found them in a friendly good humour. They wondered whether I would accompany them on a visit to their weekend home in Faiyum oasis. During my stay in Cairo I had loaned H.V. Morton's book *Through the Lands of the Bible* to Edward who told me after reading it that he owned an area of the oasis and that he had a family house there. I jumped at the invitation and arranged to meet them on a Saturday morning to be fixed when I had a weekend free from work at HQ Med/ME.

On the appointed morning I arrived at the Wissas' house in Sharia Qasrel Ali. The chauffeur was busy loading the car and he placed my hand-luggage in the boot. Edward said that the road to the oasis was nothing but a track marked by oil drums and sometimes visibility was difficult. He also said it was wise to take precautions against bandits. Marie appeared and we all climbed into the car. It was a clear morning as we set off on a journey of about fifty miles. The chauffeur drove carefully along the irregular sandy track across the Libyan desert. There were heaps of sand at the roadside deposited by sandstorms. Eventually we reached the Faiyum oasis which was a magnificent sight, set in a depression about a hundred and thirty feet deep and separated from the Nile and Pyramids by hills. There was a natural lake formed within the depression. This was full of salt water and it was possible to catch sole and other flat fish living there. Lush flora and trees abounded. We passed through a gateway into the area owned by the Wissas. Surrounded by trees and standing back was a Victorian-looking mansion. When we stopped a number of servants came out to greet us and to take the luggage. I was shown to my very pleasant and beautifully furnished bedroom and later joined my hosts for a meal. The household was very well organized, under Marie's direction. Edward took me on a tour of the estate and showed me a new weekend cottage in a rose garden which he had recently built for Marie. Edward's armed bodyguard followed us throughout the tour. I went out for another walk later on as I wanted to see and photograph the ancient dovecotes. The bodyguard pointed downwards over a bank and drew my attention to where bricks were being made without straw. They were shaped and placed in the sun to dry.

The next morning I came down to a most sumptuous breakfast. In a dish on the dining-room table were a couple of dozen small fried Egyptian chickens' eggs. There was also coffee and bacon. We spent that afternoon at Marie's new summer-house in the rose garden, talking about Edward's past educational visit to England. By sheer coincidence he had lived in Golders Green as a student and he used to frequent the Refectory Restaurant near the tube station! At last it was time for us to leave the oasis and I returned to work in Cairo.

Chapter 18

VISIT TO THE PERSIAN GULF AND LUXOR

In March 1946 my tour of duty would come to an end, so there was now only a short time remaining. Early in February I flew to the Persian Gulf and on arrival at Bahrain airfield I remember the smell of crude oil as I stepped out of the aeroplane. Sand had been compacted with oil to make a good runway surface. The station was busy in spite of the fact that there was no sign of air traffic. The next morning I sampled the airfield bath house. A huge water tank outside it was heated by oil burners. The boiling water was dispensed into the bath by manipulating a lever inside the bath house. It was all very crude but efficacious.

During my visit to Bahrain I had an invitation to visit the business area which was reached by a causeway. Here I encountered the pearl merchants conducting the sale of their glistening wares. They wore turbans and kept their pearls in little cloth bags which were stowed away within the folds of their sashes or waistbands. The merchants were assembled round a cloth-covered table and cast their pearls before possible buyers. Deals were completed over cups of strong sweet coffee and amid much excitement.

The return flight followed the oil pipeline. On arrival at Habbaniya airfield in Baghdad the heat was too much to bear and everywhere there was a shimmering heat haze. Later I walked outside the airfield entrance and came across an old Arab sitting on some carpets and rugs. The old chap was apparently well known in that area as 'Blood Orange Ali' because he had bloodshot eyes. Two rugs of similar pattern and colour caught my eye and I asked how much they were. His English was just about understandable and I gathered that the carpets came from an old mosque and that they were made in Tabriz. He said he would let me have them 'for a mere song'. As I looked interested he clapped his hands and ordered the young Arab boy who appeared to go and get some coffee. It was the usual sweetish sticky stuff cooked in a copper vessel. I squatted down by him to discuss the price and eventually I said that I would buy both rugs. He said he would accept a cheque on my London bank, which was quite a surprise in that desert environment.

Early in March I flew to Luxor accompanied by Brigadier 'Bunny' Vulliamy, who was Army Chief Signals Officer at HQ Med/ME. The sun was high and in a warm breeze the surface dust was disturbed and drifted everywhere. We had certain formalities to complete in our own spheres at the airfield. I met our signals personnel to exchange paperwork since the airfield had been in constant use during wartime.

Since a little leave was due to me I was able to stay on for a few days to visit some of the tombs and temples of the Pharaohs. We were staying at the Winter Palace Hotel which was built for the start of the tourist trade many years ago. It was comfortable and the view looking through the early morning heat haze was really exciting: honey-buff hills forming a backcloth above the Valley of the Kings — causing my imagination to dwell on the scene as it would have been thousands of years ago.

There was little tourist activity at the time so we were exceptionally privileged to move about unhindered. I was pleased to meet Aboudi, an Egyptian who had considerable archaeological knowledge of the sites situated on west and east banks of the Nile. He took us to see the tomb of the young Pharaoh King Tutankhamun, his tall figure made an imposing sight as he strode along with his horsehair fly-swatter. Of course, the fabulous and priceless treasures found in one of the chambers of Tutankhamun's tomb were by now already safely kept in the Cairo Museum. When, later, I saw these wonderful works of art I marvelled at the craftmanship of such a civilization.

Chapter 19

BACK TO CIVILIAN LIFE

Before long my return journey to the UK was settled. I left at the end of March in the capacity of OC troops, with a contingent of RAF personnel in my charge. We boarded the SS *Samaria* at Port Said, having travelled by train from Cairo along the Suez Canal railway without any mishaps. All the luggage was quickly loaded into the ship and a brief check of all ranks who were on the sailing list was carried out. Without any formal ceremony the gangplanks were withdrawn and the ship slipped away and headed out to sea.

I was pleased to find the ship's officers were friendly and was indeed glad to discover I had been allocated a comfortable cabin. The ship's engines were quiet and she skimmed the Mediterranean waves. All these conditions gave promise of a pleasant voyage all the way to Liverpool, although my responsibilities as OC troops led me to wonder what problems, if any, I would be faced with. I had to be on good terms with the Captain and his officers. They were good chaps and were helpful. I had a competent Warrant Officer on board who kept everything under control. He reported to me frequently and I was satisfied that he had the well-being of his charges at heart. Some of the airwomen were a little homesick because they had been absent from the UK for a fairly long period. Of course, we had the usual boat drill and every day I had a tour of inspection, particularly during the feeding period. All was well and at night there was plenty of entertainment — music and sing-songs — which was enjoyed by other ranks. In the evening I joined other officers and we passed the time over the odd pint, spinning yarns. On one occasion I was prompted to talk of my escapades in and around the Pyramids. While in Egypt I had had an opportunity to climb to the top of the Great Giza Pyramid. The face of the entire surface was made of blocks of stone, each roughly one metre square. This was all that was left when the original alabaster facing was removed to embellish the old mosques in Cairo's Citadel. Anyway, I explained, I found the challenge of climbing to the top a bit daunting. One had to clamber up using one's knees and to raise oneself a metre at a time. Once at the top one had to

Homeward bound on the SS Samaria — *a pen and ink sketch made by the author during the voyage.*

maintain control of one's balance, but the effort was all worth while simply because of the exquisite view of other pyramids all round.

I had plenty to talk about with the two RAF Chaplains, one a Roman Catholic and the other Church of England. My friendship with eminent Cairo Copts formed a typical subject for conversation with them. I explained it was difficult for me to understand the situation where Copts — Egyptian Christians — were to be found living close to Arab Muslims. One would think their forebears were originally Muhammadans and slowly indoctrination to the Christian faith had taken place. I had had an opportunity to visit a Coptic Church in Cairo and found the atmosphere quite similar to our C of E places of worship.

On days when the weather was warm with a fair amount of sun I used to go and sit on the ship's top deck. There I was able to make a pen and wash sketch of all the interesting things that intrigued me — ropes, radio aerials, and the huge rotating radar antenna. Yes, the sight of the radar scanner filled me with nostalgia. My mind flashed back to Fighter Command work; I thought of 'Cat's-Eyes' Cunningham and Rory Chisholm, both night fighters in 604 Squadron. Then my mind moved to 85 Squadron commanded by Peter Townsend. With our AI Mk.IV radar interception device the RAF had probed the unknown for lurking enemy bombers. The ship's system evolved from our early work and was a vital navigation aid for safety at sea and was also a probe into the unknown.

I awoke from my day-dream and looked at the finished pen sketch. It certainly looked passable. Our ship was speeding through the Bay of Biscay and the weather was changing; the warmth we had enjoyed diminishing. The next day the weather was fresh — we were now in the Irish Sea. Liverpool soon loomed up ahead and all aboard were eagerly packing and awaiting instructions. I had issued a joint Customs declaration form which had to be completed by all and sundry. Finally I had to satisfy myself that all statements were correct for all personnel. I signed to the best of my knowledge that we were not contravening Customs regulations. Before long the *Samaria* was safely moored to the quayside and disembarkation was soon completed. Some heavy luggage had to be lifted off by hoist, including the packing case containing my rugs brought back from Baghdad. The hoist unfortunately dropped this packing case which split open and I had to get ropes to make it safe. Very soon all RAF personnel evaporated, gathered up and taken away by the transport that had already been organized. I got my transport to the demobilization centre where, with great efficiency, I was checked over by the MO. I also had a chest X-ray and after a day or so I was told I was as fit as a fiddle! I could now leave and make my way homewards. Almost seven years had passed since I first reported for duty in the Royal Air Force at Yatesbury Radio School.

I arrived in London with a patched-up packing case, three heavy trunks and a suitcase. I boarded a taxi and drove out to the home of my wife's parents at Golders Green. I had a terrific reception by all present, including my wife and my own young daughters. All were well and the house was now free from the old scars of bombing. The kitchen no longer sported a Morrison air raid shelter. I walked with the family through the french doors and into the garden and noticed that, being March, all the rose bushes had recently been pruned. I could see I was going to start life afresh and adapt to yet another change of environment. I knew I would enjoy living with my own family in peace and enjoy plenty of gardening. I still had a feeling at the back of my mind that there would soon come a time when I would have to resume my own civilian scientific obligation in the X-ray engineering field. It was also quite clear that my wife and I would now have to look round for a place to settle in with our two daughters. Of course, we were eternally grateful to my parents-in-law for letting us share their home for so long. As luck would have it, Sqn/Ldr Maurice Brown of the RAAF, whom I had met in Washington during the Second World War, called one day and had tea with us all. He said he had come to tell us about a friend of his, an Australian engineer, who lived at Arkley and who wanted to sell the home which he had been building as his wife did not like the English climate and wanted to go back to Australia. We visited this Australian and were taken with the house and its surroundings. It was partly finished and still needed more to be done to it. It was just what we wanted and I immediately bought it. The house stood on high ground and the bottom of the garden had an attractive dingle with trees and small ponds. In the past this was a brick-making area and the ponds were left when the clay was dug out. We called the new home 'Dingle Ridge' because it was situated on a ridge and had a dingle at the bottom. The place had a lovely garden, an area of two acres. We moved in as soon as the house was ready in 1947. The family were excited and happy to be in a delightful country atmosphere in the county of Hertfordshire.

I soon got down to the job of planting shrubs and trees. Also, with great effort, I cut down the waist-high grass on the lawns. We had space for a summer-house and a greenhouse. My wife was tremendously happy and soon joined the social life of the village, (later becoming President of the Women's Institute). In the meantime I was comfortably settled in as Head of the Vacuum-Tube X-ray Engineering Department with my old engineering company. It was undergoing a big change, having been taken over by Metropolitan Vickers in Trafford Park, Manchester. The reorganization concerned the amalgamation with another X-ray firm called The Victor X-ray Corporation. This had links with the American General Electric Corporation. With the merger of our old firm and the Victor X-ray Corporation, the new company was to be called Newton Victor Ltd. My old managing director, Russell Wright, retired and became Chairman and our new Head was C.H. Holbeach, a delightful man. He was ex-Navy and a good engineer. I was happy with this new set-up and my job was to reorganize and re-equip our X-ray Tube Works. I was asked to visit the USA in 1948 for a couple of months to exchange engineering know-how. Also, I had to travel and purchase new production equipment such as lathes for glass fabrication of X-ray tubes and rectifying valves.

I travelled out to the USA from Southampton on the *Queen Mary*. It was mid-winter and New York habour was full of floating ice blocks. I travelled on to Milwaukee, Wisconsin, where I was to stay for several weeks. I had no difficulty in getting to know the rest of the engineering teams in the General Electric X-ray Corporation. We exchanged our ideas on X-ray tube design and vacuum process plant. One evening I was invited to have dinner with the Milwaukee's plant Vice-President, John Clough. He was a fascinating man and we got on well together when we discovered that his First World War work tallied with mine in the Second World War. I explained I was concerned with radar equipped night fighters. He said he was in England in the First World War and flew fighters at night against the Zeppelins. I told him of my childhood experience when I saw a Zeppelin after it had been shot down in flames by one of our night fighters. What a strange coincidence! While still in Milwaukee I was able to contact my World War II American companion Walter Pree, who gave me much help at the Air Ministry when we were planning to equip our Mosquitoes with SCR 720 AI.

When my tour in Milwaukee ended I returned again to the UK, this time I had the pleasure of travelling in luxury on the new *Queen Elizabeth*. She was a beautiful ship.

With the technical help I was able to get during my visit to Milwaukee our factory in Finchley soon had a really modern vacuum processing plant and we were making a wide range of high voltage rectifying valves, and X-ray tubes for the treatment of cancer were also being manufactured. We had the great task of planning engineering and production to make a 400,000 volt tube and its resonant transformer based on a design I had brought back from the GEX Corporation. It was an expensive and most sophisticated device. It was insulated by compressed gas called sulphur hexa fluoride. I had a team of engineers who tackled the design which was unorthodox, calling for a good know-how in vacuum technology. The task was certainly formidable and development problems were not easy to master when one considered all aspects of the project design. In the long run the engineering development was abandoned on economic grounds. Nevertheless the design had excellent potential.

I personally had a special design for a rotating-anode X-ray tube 'on the stocks' and I had a competent vacuum tube engineer to help with the development. Towards the end of 1952 we had a fair number of prototypes on test. I am happy to say that the first prototype model of my rotating-anode tube is now in the care of the Science Museum in London. It was technically known as the Gyromax 120 and had been used for several hundred hours in a London teaching hospital.

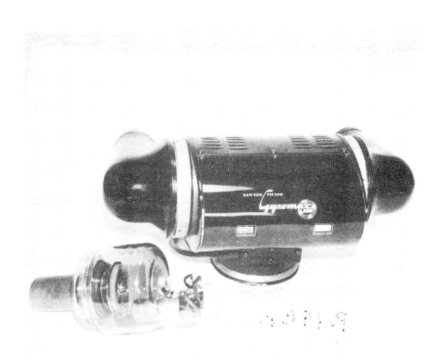

The Author's first prototype Rotating Anode X-ray Tube. The vacuum insert (British Patent Specification No. 646 274) and ray-proof shield, above, are now in the care of the Science Museum, South Kensington.

Chapter 20

COPENHAGEN CRISIS — AND AFTERWARDS

The year 1953 arrived. There was to be held the 7th International Congress of Radiology in Copenhagen. The company arranged for me to attend this congress with my wife and a number of our representatives. Travelling arrangements for UK delegates were made by the British Institute of Radiology; most of us travelled to Copenhagen by sea from Harwich.

The congress opening ceremony was held in a large public hall, His Majesty King Frederick of Denmark conducting the symphony orchestra to entertain us beforehand. There was a well-organized exhibition of radiological apparatus including a great number of our latest X-ray tubes and high-voltage rectifiers. I am proud to say that my new rotating-anode X-ray tube was taken to Copenhagen and included in this exhibition. It incorporated a revolutionary means of cooling — a feature I had been working on for over a year. Other continental and American companies had their own special equipment on show also.

Before the congress closed my wife and I had moved into the Cecil Hotel. There we were to stay for two days before going off to a prearranged meeting with an X-ray company in Paris with whom we were associated. Our stay at the Cecil Hotel ended in disaster on the morning we were due to fly to Paris. The maid had just brought us our breakfast on a tray and I was sitting up in bed enjoying a cup of coffee. My memory of what happened next is a partial blank — apparently I fell out of bed and collapsed unconscious. I remember coming round in a semi-conscious state and hearing my wife calling out and then calling on the telephone for a doctor. One came quickly and I can just remember hearing a bit of the conversation, "We must get a stretcher and get him to hospital." I later learned that I had had a cerebral haemorrhage. I was probably under sedation and next remember coming round on a hospital bed. I was being examined by one of Denmark's famous neuro-surgeons — Professor Busch. I was in a semi-stupor as he said, "I will operate you in the morning!" The next incident I recall was looking up at the business end of an X-ray tube. Vaguely I could hear the anode

148

still rotating in its evacuated glass envelope. Of course, the equipment was all part of a special device for angio radiography, in other words for X-ray diagnosis of brain disorders. My mind then went blank until vaguely I heard a muffled voice say, "Trauma!" — it must have been when I was having the operation. My mind went blank again but the next period of semi-consciousness was a joyful one — I was sitting up in bed in a private room. It was semi-dark and there bending over me was the smiling face of Mollie, my dearest wife. Within a few days I gradually regained my senses. My speech was very good and my appetite was excellent. Professor Busch came to see me and seemed satisfied with my progress. We talked together about the recent Congress of Radiology and he was surprised to hear my connection with it. He got the X-ray negatives of my brain and we discussed details on them. Every day that passed I looked forward to Mollie's visit. It is absolutely incredible to me that I was able to talk — generally one's speech is affected by such a brain haemorrhage. A little later I learnt that I nearly died during the operation and still thank the Good Lord for prolonging my life on earth by a few milli-seconds while the trauma was dealt with! Little did I know of the terrible shock Mollie suffered — everything for her was so difficult until she was able to get a real command of the situation. She did not wish to upset me with details and I made good progress. After several weeks Professor Busch told us I was fit enough to return home. Mollie contacted her cousin Willie Houston in BOAC about getting me out of Copenhagen by air. He master-minded the flight and made transport arrangements from Heathrow to get me home by ambulance. We said 'goodbye' to the Professor and boarded a taxi to the airport. *En route* Mollie asked the taxi driver to stop at a church in the city. She desperately wished to offer her prayers of thanks for my progress — a good Christian act I shall never forget. We were ushered into an ambulance on leaving the aeroplane, thanks to the help given by the airline. Soon I was safely back at 'Dingle Ridge' to be greeted by my two young daughters and our good neighbourly friends the McFeeters, with whom the children had been staying while I was ill, and who had kept an eye on our home. My head was covered in a turban of cotton wool and bandages and I stayed like that until I was able to visit the London Hospital for a check up in the Neurological department. I stayed at home like a cabbage until gradually, with my wife's care, I began to feel like my old normal self. I had a final report that all was well and started to do work in the garden. Of course, this sudden illness had had considerable repercussions at my engineering works. Most of my engineers had left the company and the manufacture of my X-ray project had been terminated. I relinquished the position as Head of our X-ray tube and vacuum engineering works and started to do some studies on the subject of contact micro-radiography. This work appealed to me, being a professional photographer. A whole year passed and I had continued my studies using soft X-rays and had a number of interesting micro-radiographs. So much so, I was asked to read a paper on my work before the Institute of Non-Destructive Testing at a convention in Chester. I had studied small biological specimens, materials of low density such as butterfly wings and bird feathers. My last radiograph was of a dragon-fly's eye — a picture of this work is included.

At about this period I persuaded my wife to take up her painting again — she had spent so much of her time on me. I equipped her with all necessary brushes and paints and her father was kind enough to have a cedar wood studio built in our garden so all was set up for her. She specialized in flower painting and after a few years had a one-woman show. As a therapeutic help I also started painting in oils, although I was a keen water-colourist. We both joined the local art societies: The Barnet Guild of Artists and The Stanmore Art Society.

My old urge to return to X-ray engineering came back to me and, being now fully recovered, I joined Elliott Electronic Tubes Limited in Borehamwood, where I had the interesting job as Chief Health Physicist in the Vacuum Physics Laboratory. This gave me ample scope to practise my radiation knowledge — ensuring that the radiation level conformed with statutory regulations as laid down in the Factory Act, and so on. In most cases the source of radiation was either X-rays, radio-isotopes, or even a generator producing neutrons. In connection with the latter, gamma rays sometimes presented problems since I was responsible for the safety and health of personnel. I was asked to develop a special clean room. The environment had to be ideal temperature and humidity-wise to be acceptable physically and indeed the air breathed by the operator had to be ultra-clean. The freedom from dust particles was essential to prevent contamination of the components handled in the clean-room environment. This was an intriguing exercise calling for an air filtration of 0.5 microns of any particles stopped by the air filters. The personnel were issued with lint-free anti-static garments. Human hair and beards had also to be covered. Special plastic shoes were donned before entering the clean-room. In fact, the entire structure of the clean-room was faced with a smooth plastic surface.

Later on the company changed its name to Marconi Avionics and

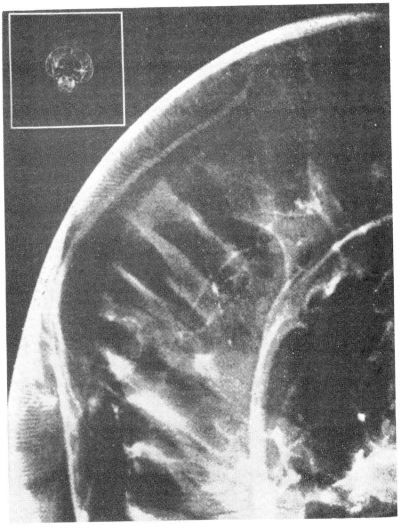

Micro-radiograph of a dragon-fly's eye taken with 8 kV soft X-rays

after a number of years of service I eventually retired at the age of sixty-six. I settled down and was indeed busy with my garden. My other hobby was photography. I took a series of macro photographs of flowers and other botanical subjects. I still spent some time doing oil painting, and my wife and I were supremely happy working together. It was therefore a terrible blow when Mollie developed cancer. She had an operation and was some time at home convalescing. Later, for the good of her health, we flew to California to stay with Mollie's cousin Bob Savage and family. They gave us a wonderful reception and went to enormous trouble to look after her health. They planned a special tour visiting the Grand Canyon and finishing at Colorado where we stayed with another cousin John Savage, a shale-oil expert, in his lovely home at Rifle. We next visited Mollie's cousin Grace Savage who lived in Washington, having retired from Government service. The local airline got us to Denver on time, with beautiful mountain scenery *en route*. The main airline then took us to Washington where we had a short and enjoyable stay. On our first day we visited the State Rooms of the White House by courtesy of Ronald Reagan.

On our return to the UK we stopped over in New York where we had a comfortable stay with my niece Louise, the wife of the BBC representative in the city, Paul Reynolds. I was glad to be able to take Mollie to the Metropolitan Museum where we thoroughly enjoyed seeing the fine collection of paintings by Monet. Our homeward flight to the UK was uneventful.

The next year was hectic — Mollie continued to do her oil paintings and had a collection ready for submission to the United Artists Exhibition at the Mall Gallery. During this period of the year she was far from well and complained of tiredness — in fact she had developed secondary cancer and was taken into hospital in July where she died on the 20th July. It was very sad that she had been too ill to see her six paintings on exhibition at the Mall Gallery and I am very proud that she was posthumously awarded full membership of the Society of United Artists. All Arkley was stunned by her death and I simply could not believe what had happened. I continued to live on at our dream house 'Dingle Ridge' until a year or so later I decided to make a change and to start life afresh. On 16th August 1985 I moved into a fairly new bungalow with a smallish garden situated beside the green belt with a fine country meadow view. I am now comfortably installed and have a garden which will grow most of Mollie's favourite flowers. I have some of Mollie's last family portraits in addition to all her lovely flower

Radiation laboratory showing the neutron generator being lifted out of its test-cell. The Health Physicist probes the source using his radiation monitor. Painting by the author.

paintings which had been on exhibition at the Mall Gallery. I feel certain she would have been pleased that I decided to put pen to paper. I only hope the reader will appreciate the fact that I have tried to give a fairly full and accurate account of my life's work!

Without Mollie's encouragement I could not have achieved my aim in life.

Over seventy years have passed since my early childhood. I think of my brother and sister. Both had distinguished careers. Alas they are no longer alive.

I have enjoyed my life with all its facets — good, humorous and sometimes sad — which have had a considerable influence on the writing of these memoirs.

NOCTURN IN RETROSPECT
by N.C. Cordingly, October 1986

Oh! How the AIs did scan!
Good Show! 'Lucero' and 'Loran'.
'Perfectos', too, was a wizard homer,
Guiding us back when each sortie was over.
All praise to radar and RCM,
Not forgetting our Signals 'gen'.
Codes and ciphers have done us proud —
"Bang on! Whizz Oh!" we cried aloud.
And now everywhere the Hun war is over —
Peace at last from John O'Groats to Dover.

EPILOGUE

Forty-one years after the end of the Second World War, I was privileged to attend a reunion luncheon party given in September 1986 by my Chief Signals Officer, Group Captain Sam Goodman, CBE.

Distinguished RAF night fighter colleagues Air Commodore Rory Chisholm, CBE, DSO, DFC, and Group Captain John (Cat's Eyes) Cunningham, DSO, DFC, were present.

The photograph was taken at the reunion party. Left to right: Sam, Author, Rory, John.

The passing of Air Vice-Marshal Addison (Addy) of HQ 100 (Bomber Support) Group

My story would not be complete without a further mention of my last RAF Chief, Addy, with whom I served whilst working on radio countermeasures in conjunction with our airborne radar equipped night fighter offensive. In July 1987 news reached me that Addy had died after a long illness.

By courtesy of the *Daily Telegraph* I reproduce a copy of the obituary:

Air Vice-Marshal 'Addy' Addison, who has died aged 88, was the signals specialist upon whom 'Bomber' Harris relied to counter Germany's effective ground and night fighter defences in the middle of the 1939-45 war.

Such was Harris's confidence, that in 1943 'Addy' was entrusted with the new 100 (Bomber Support) Group, its radio countermeasures squadrons devoted to reducing Bomber Command's mounting losses.

Addison's success in wearing down the enemy radio, radar and fighter defences, resulted from his single-minded career-long accumulation of electrical, wireless and signals expertise and brilliant conduct of 'electronic warfare.'

Almost 17 when he joined the Royal Flying Corps from Southgate County School as a 2nd Air Mechanic in 1915, Edward Barker Addison was soon promoted 1st Air Mechanic, becoming Corporal in 1917. A year afterwards he was commissioned in the newly-formed RAF.

After the 1914-18 War, he went up to Sidney Sussex College, Cambridge, graduating in natural science in 1921. Returning to the RAF, he was recommissioned as a pilot officer in the General Duties Branch and received his wings in 1922.

After serving three years in India, Addison returned to marry Blanche Rosain, a French student he had met at Cambridge.

Addison's war-within-the-war, the 'Battle of the Beams', began towards the end of August, 1940, when the Luftwaffe started to supplement its daylight Battle of Britain raids with heavy night attacks guided by transmitting stations operating a beam apparatus known as 'Knickebein'.

He was ordered to form 80 Wing at Radlett, Herts, to counter enemy beams. Equipment was scarce and scrappy, but Addison managed to jam enemy transmitters with adapted hospital radio-therapy sets.

From April 1942, Addison was successively Deputy Director and Director of Signals at the Air Ministry. By the autumn of 1943 the tide was turning.

As the RAF went from the defensive to the offensive, 100 (Bomber Support) Group, embodying 80 Wing, was formed within Bomber Command with Addison as its leader.

He launched a campaign to jam, spoof and generally confuse Luftflotte Reich defences. The group also had its own long-range fighters, equipped with Serrate radio-homing devices for intercepting night fighters.

Planning such operations, driving on scientific developments to keep pace with rapid enemy counter-action, Addison achieved nothing less than the preservation of Bomber Command as a strong operational force.